PUGS AND DRUMMERS

Also by John Marchington

Your Book of Photographing Wildlife

Shooting—A Complete Guide for Beginners

An Introduction to Bird and Wildlife Photography (with Anthony Clay, A.R.P.S.)

Sportsman's Bag

Game Shooting—Management and Economics

The Practical Wildfowler

Pugs and Drummers

FERRETS AND RABBITS IN BRITAIN

John Marchington

with photographs by the author

Faber and Faber

LONDON BOSTON

First published in 1978
by Faber and Faber Limited
3 Queen Square London WC1
Printed in Great Britain by
Latimer Trend & Company Ltd, Plymouth

British Library Cataloguing in Publication Data

Marchington, John
Pugs and drummers.
1. Rabbits 2. Ferrets
I. Title
599'.322 QL737.L32

ISBN 0-571-11204-8

Dedicated to

Arthur Hall—

for reasons to be explained later

Contents

Illustrations

All photographs, including that on the jacket, were taken by the author

Acknowledgements

My thanks are due to the following:

To Anthony Jackson, Editor of *Shooting Times and Country Magazine*, who, in spite of a life immersed in the literature of field sports, found the time and patience to write the foreword.

To those people who so kindly corresponded with me over my ideas and theories, and in particular Dr. A. J. Sutcliffe of the Department of Palaeontology of the British Museum; Dr. D. F. Mayhew of the Geologisch Instituut der Universiteit Utrecht, Netherlands; Dr. A. J. Stuart of the Department of Zoology, University of Cambridge; Dr. D. H. Maling of the Department of Geography, University College of Swansea; and Mr. H. W. Mackworth-Praed, F.R.E.S., F.R.G.S., of the Surrey Trust for Nature Conservation.

To Collins for permission to quote from *The Rabbit* by Thompson and Worden; to David and Charles for permission to quote from *Rabbits and Their History* by John Sheail; to André Deutsch for permission to quote from the *Private Life of the Rabbit* by R. M. Lockley, (also available in paperback from Corgi Books).

To the Country Landowners' Association and Peter Whitaker for permission to use the title 'Pugs and Drummers', for which the Association enjoys the copyright.

To the editors of *Shooting Times and Country Magazine* and *The Field* for permission to reproduce some of my photographs which have previously appeared in their publications.

And, finally, to my wife Janet who has performed the lengthy task of typing this manuscript with her usual mixture of efficiency and enthusiasm.

Foreword

Unlike the majority, I suspect, of foreword writers I have actually taken the trouble to read the book which I am forewording. The art of foreword writing, like that of the reviewer, largely consists of a swift flick at the chapter headings, a hasty glance through to make sure the author is not being beastly about any of the writer's cherished shibboleths and some background knowledge enabling one to assure the reader that the man behind the book is 'one of us'.

Well, as I said before, I have consumed this book from page one to the final sentence, becoming increasingly absorbed as I did so. Books like this tend to give me an inferiority complex. As a writer I know a little about the consumption of midnight oil, the grind involved in research, the diligence and painstaking care called for if one is to be accurate and to provide interest, information and new angles on a subject. John Marchington, whom I have known for many moons as a shooting man extraordinary and photographer *par excellence*, told me that when he set out on his rabbit and ferret quest he thought, foolish fellow, that he might have to read half-a-dozen books for background material. He ended up with forty-four books tucked away under his belt! His assiduity is apparent as he delves into the histories of the drummer (rabbit) and the pug (ferret). Claims and counter-claims, theories about Roman and Normans—the web is indeed tangled and made more intricate by the constant repetition over the years of authors quoting as fact half-truths whose origins are perhaps lost in the mists of antiquity. The author unerringly threads his way through the maze, placing before us the evidence so carefully assembled and drawing conclusions which are notable for their balanced logic.

I rather suspect that this book, like Topsy, just growed and growed. From perhaps a modest suggestion of a history of the rabbit and its musteline opponent the ferret, it has grown to what I feel sure must become that relative rarity in the world of sporting books—a classic.

You may perhaps feel that a creature as common as the rabbit and one as relatively well-known as the ferret have both had maximum press exposure. Can further be said? J. M. categorically shows us that not only has it not all been said, but that, as is so often the case with a familiar creature, there is still an enormous amount to learn.

Don't run away with the idea that the covers of this book enclose a dusty, exhaustive and tedious catalogue of research. Written lucidly and with humour, the author covers the practical side of sport with ferret and rabbit and, most important, the care of ferrets. Like me, he believes that a healthy and happy ferret will be found living in a spacious open run with warm comfortable quarters. Not for us the cramped, frequently dirty and dark hutches littered with damp bedding and the remains of mouldering corpses or spilt bread and milk. Today's ferret is emancipated and the sooner the message is driven home the better.

What more can I say? Nothing, except if you are casually reading this foreword prior to a purchase, hesitate no longer; you will not, I can assure you with hand on heart, regret a single penny and may well open the doorway to a whole new world of sport, good food (the author will not touch rabbits since myxomatosis—fair enough but he is missing some super grub) and constant interest.

Tony Jackson

Introduction

This work began as a simple enough project—a desire to write a book touching on all aspects of rabbits and ferrets, and intended to meet the new interest in both, arising from the recovery in rabbit numbers. Principally, I had in mind the generation of sportsmen who grew up hardly seeing a wild rabbit—never mind experiencing the thrills of stalking down a hedge with their first ·410—setting their first snare or owning their own ferret. But beyond this clear-cut group I had in mind my own generation, and older ones, to whom rabbits and ferrets were once numbered among the good, exciting things of life, and who, through the lean years of heavy myxomatosis, looked back with nostalgia.

And so I set to what appeared a straight forward task only to discover quickly that an apparently simple subject was actually surprisingly complex. Every question I sought to answer led me down several side-roads which, in turn, branched in several directions and, as a glance at the bibliography at the end of the book will show, I eventually read no fewer than forty-four books in researching the subject, and spent much of my spare time for eight months gathering material before I commenced writing. But, significantly, although the work involved was much greater than expected the task of writing this book has been a fascinating one. *Pugs and Drummers* has had its difficult stretches, but the enthusiasm which developed as my knowledge grew has swept over them. No book has given me greater pleasure to write and I can only hope that some of this will be reflected back to its readers.

This is a convenient point to explain why this book is dedicated to Arthur Hall, whose name will be totally unfamiliar to you. Arthur is my Norfolk uncle, by whom, as a very small boy, I was introduced to the pursuit of the rabbit and to his hutches of assorted ferrets. I would not trouble you with this slice of personal nostalgia were it not for the fact that Arthur is one of a unique generation, for his life spans the gap between two very different worlds. Born towards the end of the last century, he began farm work at the age of thirteen and followed a pattern which had hardly changed for generations. Food was produced by very hard physical work, partly horses', partly men's, and hours were long and wages small. By the time he retired, horses were a novelty and farm workers were skilled technicians, controlling complex and expensive machinery. To talk to Arthur is to gain a vivid picture of the old agriculture—the unending toil softened by contact with nature and the honest simplicity of the work. 'Topping' beet by hand in a freezing wind or hand-milking a dozen cows at dawn seven days a week was a harsh existence, but it forged characteristics sadly absent nowadays. Of greater relevance to this book is his attitude to rabbits and ferrets for he personifies the ageless countryman. His ancestors, and mine for that matter, must have set innumerable snares and gins, kept ferrets uncountable, walked gingerly in the dark down many a wood-side with a long-net in a sack on their backs and taken rabbits by the thousand. He warrants his dedication as the representative of all the countrymen who have had a sharp eye for a drummer and a soft heart for a pug.

Freely and unashamedly I admit to taking my title from the Game Fair Exhibition of that name, and I am grateful to the organizers for permission to do so. The Game Fair itself is, of course, the sporting showpiece of The Country Landowners' Association, and attendance has become almost an annual pilgrimage for the followers of field sports in Britain. In 1974 Peter Whitaker, the editor of the Association's journal, conceived the idea of an Exhibition at the Fair to deal exclusively with rabbits and ferrets. It was an instant success, and the throngs that surrounded it at that and every subsequent Game Fair are an indication of the interest that attaches to Pugs (ferrets) and Drummers (rabbits). Rabbits obviously earned the slang term of 'drummers' through the habit of drumming their hind feet on the ground to warn others of the approach of danger. How the ferret became to be called a 'pug' is less clear, although a likely reason is its pug nose; an alternative derivation could come from its pugnacious temperament. Reputedly the terms were used by old-time Berkshire poachers and mouchers trying to keep their discussions confidential. It would be interesting to find out how much the various visitors to the Pugs and Drummers Exhibition know about rabbits and ferrets, and why they go. Some will know nothing and visit out of curiosity. Others will go for a specific purpose: to ask a question, swop a ferret, or watch nets being made. But, I suspect, the majority go simply because they share my instinctive liking and interest for rabbits and ferrets. Of course, so far as rabbits are concerned, we have been brain-washed from our nursery days to like them. Beatrix Potter started the trend in our infant minds and about the time her influence was beginning to wane our father, or a keeper or some other friendly countryman, spoke of guns, ferrets, snares and nets, and we saw the rabbit in a different light. Most sportsmen possess this weird trait, quite inexplicable to town dwellers, of loving the things they pursue, and this enthusiasm for the rabbit is not limited to any one social level. Patrick Chalmers, of the ever-beguiling pen said, with truth, in *At the Sign of the Dog and Gun*, 'Beaters too, boys to greybeards, would a thousand times rather kick a rabbit up for you than send a ten score of cock pheasants forward to the Guns.' And the Guns themselves, plus-two'd and necktied, see how they stiffen and alert at the bounce and white scut of a rabbit in the brambles. In all probability the rule will be 'no ground game', but the rabbit will have struck a special chord, particularly in that part of their minds which is nearest to the boy.

Other major authors on the rabbit reflect Chalmers's view. Lockley said the rabbit is endowed with much charm. Thompson and Worden said that no matter how great a pest rabbits were they would always swerve to avoid running one over. Tommy Turner, the late Head Keeper at Elveden, wrote on the subject of elderly beaters, 'Some of the old ones would hardly open their mouths all day except when feeding or drinking, but put them amongst the rabbits and they would hop about as nimbly as the boys and yell with the best of them.' And there you have it—there is something about the rabbit that arouses the primitive hunting instinct within us to a far greater degree than its more lordly cousins of the field, wood or hill. Nor can we dismiss the rabbit as a simple creature. It is, as we will see later, much more interesting and complex than most people realize.

I find it hard to explain the affection that undoubtedly exists for the ferret; it is not just the link with enjoyable sport that prompts many of us, for a surprising number of people who have no prior knowledge of them show an immediate liking. Perhaps it is the endearing qualities of liveliness and curiosity, or the bright keen eyes and sharp little face. Certainly they appeal to the fair sex to a surprising degree. On many occasions we have introduced ours to women guests of the home with, I will admit, a slight tinge of anticipatory wickedness, only to find them admired and freely handled. I will never forget one visitor with a country background, who, resplendent in evening dress and jewellery, plunged her nose into the coat of one of our polecat ferrets and exclaimed, 'Oh, that wonderful smell again!'

Men, if you think about it, have always been very fond of domesticated predators. Hawks are a good example and a pack of hounds is a better one. No doubt a psychologist would tell us that to control a predator is good for a man's ego and is but little separated from the use of a gun. Or it may be a mix of this with memories of childhood days, for what country boy, with the exception of the deprived generation, failed to own a ferret at some stage. One brief tale will serve to underline the natural feeling of most men towards ferrets. My family and I were on the Isle of Mull; it was evening and we were chatting to one of the local Forestry Commission workers who was reputed to be a mine of information on local natural history. To be more accurate we were trying to chat, but the going was very hard. By nature a quiet, dour man, seeing few strangers, our presence obviously embarrassed him and the atmosphere was tense and conversation entirely one way. By chance I mentioned we had a ferret with us and for the first time he showed interest. One of the boys fetched it and as we handed it to him, his eyes lit up. He relaxed, glowed with warmth, looked into its eyes, stroked it and said, 'Och—that's a bonny wee beast.' From that moment on he behaved as if we were friends of many years. I would not claim quite the same dramatic effect in every case, but it is a rare countryman who has no regard for ferrets. In part this is because ferrets, properly kept that is, are intelligent little creatures with their own individual characters. As an example, in the long, hot summer of 1976 our pack burrowed into the ground in their run and formed a cool underground chamber. The days were spent in this and they emerged only for food or the cool of the evening. A friend's ferret, confined to a hutch, bit off all the body hair it could reach.

To put ferreting into perspective I must concede that it is not a major field sport, nor can I pretend that I now spend a lot of time at it. There was a time, as a youngster in the Derbyshire hills, when every grey Sunday dawn saw me pedalling up into the snow-coated hills with a load of ferrets and equipment. Now the pace and demands of life are too great, but I still accompany my sons when time permits and live the past again in their eager enthusiasm. It is a pleasure to cast aside all pressures and problems and relax in this most simple and basic of sports.

It is in much the same spirit that I have written this book. None of the matters with which it deals are of any real consequence to humanity, but perhaps that is its virtue.

My detailed aim was two-fold—to mix together practical information on ferreting and rabbiting as a sport with a great deal of other relevant information, some useful and some useless but fascinating. No book that I could discover has yet done this. Some covered the natural history of the rabbit in depth, but never mentioned sport. Others were expert on ferreting but ignored other ways of pursuing rabbits. The strictly historical disregarded practical matters. And so on. Here is gathered a hotch-potch, compiled from personal experience, some original thinking and a mass of gleanings of the work of others.

In researching the work of others it soon became obvious to me that the degree of reliability of my sources varied widely, depending in some part upon whether the author was a scientist or a layman. A good scientist will never accept a loose or general statement, and expects to be able to prove all his assertions with either his own work or that of another scientist. The layman, on the other hand, is not over-fussy about his sources as long as they either support his views or lend colour to his writing. This leads to suppositions, shifts of emphasis and exaggerations. Although both laymen and scientists often lean heavily on the work of earlier writers they vary greatly, too, in the extent to which they pay credit. Some are generous in their tributes and others make no mention, giving, perhaps unintentionally, the impression that the knowledge is their own. I kept a sharp look-out for such repetition, partly to see if misconceptions were being furthered, but also for the pleasure of playing a form of literary gamekeeper and being able to think, 'Now my lad—that's not your original work!' Let me demonstrate the point with an actual instance. In his book *Rabbits and Their History* (1971), Sheail, discussing the attitude of rabbits to damp, wrote, 'Rabbits are, in fact, more resistant than sheep and on one estate in Mull, for example, twenty per cent of the sheep died owing to the wetness of the ground whereas the rabbits flourished.' So be it; twenty per cent of the sheep died through wetness. Weeks later memory rang a bell when I read a passage in Simpson's *The Wild Rabbit in a New Aspect* (1895), 'The owner of an estate in Mull, where the rainfall is very heavy and continuous in winter, writes me that rabbits abound there, large numbers being despatched weekly to England, adding that, he doubts if it be worth while fighting such a wet climate by producing sheep, among which the mortality often amounts to twenty per cent, whereas the rabbits do well.' It is possible but unlikely that Sheail had another source for his statistics and 'often amounts to twenty per cent' hardens to a firm death-rate of twenty per cent. Add to this the fact that the Mull estate owner was also probably guilty of a layman's exaggeration for effect and the truth is distorted. It is, I accept, not a major deviation and neither are we concerned with sheep, but it illustrates my point that constant repetition leads to distortion. As a further instance, Sheail (of whom I will shortly speak highly!) wrote, on the subject of the rabbit's feeding attitude towards plants, 'they tend to avoid woody, spiney, hairy, stinging and poisonous plants.' He gives no reference, and it is possible he conducted his own experiments, but I am more inclined to connect his view with a statement in Thompson and Worden's book (1956), which quoted Tansley as saying, 'those which are woody, spiney, hairy, stinging and poisonous are usually avoided.'

The literature for which laymen have been responsible is particularly suspect on the question of ferrets, ferreting and poaching, for so much has been hearsay from uneducated men recorded by others with little practical experience.

Even eminently practical laymen are guilty of errors if they fall into the trap of making positive statements beyond their certain experience. Consider Samuel and Lloyd in *Rabbiting and Ferreting*, a booklet published by the British Field Sports Society and frequently praised. On page 7 (7th edition, 1972). we read, 'There is no "pairing off" even for a season', a statement which is partially but not wholly true; and on page 8, 'Rabbits are real slum dwellers who delight in overcrowded conditions.' This is quite wrong, as reference to chapter 3 will show. These errors do not alter the wealth of sound practical advice contained in the booklet, but they are examples of practical men going beyond the extent of their personal knowledge and making inaccurate categorical statements. Again on page 7 appears 'There is no special time when rabbits breed. I have found young rabbits in every month of the year.' Whichever of the authors wrote this has concluded quite wrongly that because he has found young rabbits in every month of the year, rabbits must breed freely throughout the year. In fact there is a clearly defined breeding season as chapter 4 shows.

The more hours I spent reading, the more clearly it emerged that there are relatively few really excellent books by men who know their subject extremely well. There are many more by authors who have a passing acquaintance with some aspect and draw deeply from these few authorities. Part of my pleasure has been to search for the truth, enquiring into every unanswered question and keeping an open mind on unsubstantiated statements. On many occasions I will be quoting from other works, many of them now out of print, and some of these are well worth reading for their content, their style, and for the glimpses they give into an age now gone for ever. This book would be incomplete if I failed to present a brief list of these various authorities. (For a full list of books drawn upon see the bibliography on pp. 209–13.)

Foremost among the scientific works is *The Rabbit* by Harry V. Thompson and Alastair N. Worden, first published in 1956 by Collins in The New Naturalist series. It is all that a book by a pair of lively-minded scientists should be—bursting with information, easy to read and strictly accurate. The coverage is immense, extending even to such obscure aspects as the fauna of rabbit carcasses, but one never loses the feeling that the authors write with feeling and not simply as detached scientists. It falls short only on the history of myxomatosis in Britain for it was written just after the disease arrived. At the moment of writing it is out of print but it warrants a new issue and will doubtless get it.

Another notable book written by a scientist is R. M. Lockley's *The Private Life of the Rabbit*, originally published by André Deutsch in 1964, and then as a Corgi paperback in 1973. Lockley's first encounter with rabbits began when, as a young man, he leased the island of Skokholm and set about the task of eliminating the rabbit population so that he could realize his ambition of breeding Chinchilla rabbits in a wild state. Two years and several thousand dead rabbits later he abandoned the attempt, having gained a deep respect for the ability of the rabbit to survive. From 1954 to 1959 he carried out a life-history study of the rabbit on a private estate in Pembrokeshire and his book catalogues the results. Viewed from the strictly scientific angle it is not above criticism, but it is a remarkable document, which not only informs but leaves the reader with a strong affection for the animal. In fact Lockley's book was the inspiration for Richard Adams's best-seller, *Watership Down.*

Moving, by degrees, from the scientific towards the purely practical, the next step is John Sheail's *Rabbits and their History*, published by David & Charles in 1971. In spite of my criticism of minor details, this is a really excellent work. The title describes the contents, but gives no indication of the thoroughness and extent of the coverage. It is not a book of an author's opinions but a meticulous sifting through of a wide range of material. It is essential reading for anyone who really wants to gain a wide grasp of the part the rabbit has played in the countryside.

Next comes the book to which I would award the first prize for its breadth of coverage—James Edmund Harting's *The Rabbit*, published in 1898 by Longman's Green & Co. in the celebrated Fur, Feather and Fin series. Harting combined the ability to write well with both scientific and practical knowledge and the result was a work packed with sound, practical advice and experiences. Not for Harting the loose comment or unsubstantiated statistics—time after time he verifies his statements with names, addresses and dates. He draws deep, quoting one moment from Pliny and Shakespeare and the next from a contemporary gamekeeper. Many unacknowledged statements made by subsequent authors can, with a little detective work, be shown to have emanated from Harting. In my view nothing published before or since covers the subject in general terms so well. Of course, in some aspects of natural history he is now seen to be in error, but this does nothing to detract from the pleasure to be found in its pages. Among my antiquarian books is a slim volume by Harting called *Hints on Shore Shooting* (1871), which credits him with being the author of *The Birds of Middlesex*, etc. He is also given the qualifications of F.L.S., F.Z.S., but surprisingly did not use these in *The Rabbit*. This latter is, of course, long since out of print and secondhand copies are well worth buying as an investment.

Next come the purely practical books. Many are repetitive, but a few are excellent. One such, by Nicholas Everitt, *Ferrets: Their Management in Health and Disease*, published in 1906, is remarkable for the details and illustrations of various hutches, courts and traps. It has not the authoritative ring of later works on the actual business of ferreting, but it shows how seriously ferrets and ferreting were regarded at the turn of the century.

Quite the smallest, cheapest and best booklet—one cannot call it a book—on ferreting was *Ferrets and Ferreting*, written by Arthur Niblett and the editor of *The Exchange and Mart*. It is a fifty-eight page publication on cheap absorbent paper with a glossy paper cover, and now long out of print. It was published by The Bazaar, Exchange and Mart Ltd. and the earliest version (anonymous) was printed in London in 1875. Mine is the eleventh edition, and priced 2s. I paid £3 for it and was fortunate for the usual price is £5. The writers were obviously men who kept, bred and worked ferrets, and subsequent writers have paid them the compliment of plagiarizing their work shamelessly. When, later in this book, I quote from this publication, I refer only to Niblett, who thus becomes the codeword. (Serve the editor right for concealing his identity!)

The library of any serious student of the rabbit would be incomplete without *The Wild Rabbit in a New Aspect or Rabbit-*

Warrens that Pay by J. Simpson, published in 1895. Simpson was the wood-agent on the Wortley Hall Park Estate of the Earl of Wharncliffe, and both he and his employer were interested in rabbit-farming. Rabbit-farming as such had been carried on for centuries in the conventional warrens but Simpson believed that warren management was imperfectly understood and carried out very haphazardly. With the encouragement of the Earl he built a well-equipped experimental warren and the book is a most interesting record of his experiments, results and theories. Simpson was successful in dramatically increasing the rabbit-yield per acre and, in other times, his ideas would have been widely adopted. The book is valuable not only for its application to the central theme, but also for the side-lights it throws on other issues.

Among the purely practical books William Thomas's *Rabbit Shooting to Ferrets* (1946), has not over the years received the credit it deserves. In the multitude of works offering very similar advice this one bears the stamp of an author who has great experience in everything he writes about. There is nothing hesitant about Thomas—his statements are always positive and precise, in fact too precise for such an unpredictable activity as ferreting. But even allowing for this it is certainly the best and most comprehensive book on *ferreting* that I have read. The jacket cover, incidentally, is one of the rare sources supporting the belief that the Romans introduced the rabbit. Not the least of the good things to be found within is a short poem by the author, entitled 'Boxing Day':

A clear blue sky, a frosty morn,
A soft and kindly breeze,
A radiant sun to warm the earth,
filtering through the trees;
Some ferrets scrabbling in their sack,
the spaniel at the door,
Companion gun, flask, sandwiches;
What *could* man wish for more?

So far my recommendations have dealt with instructional books but as the object of this book is more than simple instruction, I am anxious to introduce you to H. C. Barkley's *Studies in the Art of Rat-Catching*, published in 1896. I discovered this little gem by pure accident, thought it might be useful, bought it for very little and began to read it in the belief that I would be instructed in catching rats by a simple rat-catcher. Nor, in the first few pages was I disillusioned: 'In those days, and during all my active life, I have had to work to live, owing to the constant scarcity of rats.' However, it quickly emerged from the quality of the writing that here was a man of scholarship, writing with his tongue in his cheek and a twinkle in his eye. To the end he maintains his humble calling. 'One last word. If in the following pages you come across a bit of grammar or spelling calculated to make a Head Master sit up, excuse it, and remember that I have been a rat-catcher all my life, and that as a class we are not quite A 1 at book learning.' My own guess is that he was a Public School teacher, for he begins, 'Ever since I was a boy and ah! long, long before that, I fancy, the one great anxiety of parents of the upper and middle classes blessed with large families has been "What are we to do with our boys?" ' The answer he proposes is to make them rat-catchers, a solution one can imagine appealing to the sense of humour of a man constantly troubled by the concern of fee-paying parents for their sons. Warming to his subject he later addresses a few words to headmasters, 'Admirable as their academies are for turning out Greek and Latin scholars, I cannot help thinking a proper provision is seldom made in their establishments for acquiring a real working knowledge of the profession of a rat-catcher; and I wish to suggest that it would be as well to insist on all those students who wish to take up this subject keeping at school at least one good dog and a ferret, and that two afternoons a week should be set apart entirely for field practice, and that the cost of this should be jotted down at the end of each term in the little school account that is sent home to the student's parents.'

It is a delightful little book, and concealed in the humour there lies a great deal of practical, good advice on ferrets and ferreting. For those who would like to do some detective work on Barkley's profession the title page shows that he also wrote, among others, *My Boyhood* and *Between the Danube and the Black Sea*.

Many other excellent works mention rabbits and ferrets, including such classics as Charles St. John's *Wild Sports of the Highlands* (1879) and Sir Ralph Payne-Gallwey's *Letters to Young Shooters*

(4th edition, 1895), but they merely touch on them, quickly returning to those creatures generally regarded as of greater importance, such as stags, grouse, pheasants and the like. We will not be lured by these glamous distractions, but concentrate our thoughts loyally on the humble rabbit and ferret and, in so doing, be rewarded with much of interest.

CHAPTER ONE

Enter the Rabbit

Although this book is concerned with both rabbits and ferrets, the main spotlight must be focused upon the rabbit. For centuries this quiet and timid creature has played a minor, but constant, part in the story of the countryside. Untold thousands of shooting men have recorded their first heart-stopping kill with a rabbit; thousands more, less fortunate, have relied on them to feed their families; men have been jailed and even transported for poaching them; and this humble creature has received a surprising amount of time from both parliament and the law. Take away the rabbit and some of the colour goes from the backcloth of country life. The ferret, however, is just a bit player, off-stage for the most part, and brought on for moments of occasional drama. Without the rabbit the ferret would be a curiosity, restricted to ratting for sport.

So the rabbit takes its prior bow, and we reach the fascinating question of when it first arrived with us. There is no decisive evidence on when or how the rabbit reached this country and all authors who have dealt seriously with the rabbit have attempted their own conclusion. With one or two exceptions these fall into one of two schools of thought—that rabbits were introduced either by the Romans or from France between the eleventh and thirteenth centuries. Both theories have good arguments in their favour, but the case for a Norman introduction appears strongest. It is put so well by Thompson and Worden in *The Rabbit*, that a brief synopsis of their view is warranted. The first undoubted records of rabbits in Britain do not occur, they say, until the thirteenth century. There are records of ferreting in 1272 and of 2,000 rabbit skins being taken from Lundy Island in 1274. Shortly after the rabbit became an important meat at feasts, and in 1309 at Canterbury it appears to have been rated as highly as sucking pig. From the fact that they fetched a high price in the thirteenth and fourteenth centuries Thompson and Worden conclude that it is unlikely they had spread to many parts of the country. They continue, 'In 1389, conynges, warrens and ferrets made their first appearance in the statute book and in the fourteenth and fifteenth centuries, rabbits formed part of the menus at great feasts, such as the Coronation of Henry IV in 1399, and the stalling of the Archbishop of Canterbury in 1443, and the installation of "George Nevill, Archbishop of York and Chancelour of Englande", in 1465—when there were 4000 conies on the bill of fare.'

Essentially, then, Thompson and Worden are saying that there is no evidence of the existence of the rabbit here prior to the thirteenth century, but that after that time mention became common. They state positively that there is no evidence of introduction by the Romans; that Julius Caesar does not refer to it; and there is no mention of warrens in Domesday Book (1086).

Sheail supports Thompson and Worden, and for the same reason, saying, 'There are no references to rabbits in the British Isles before 1066.' He mentions that rabbit bones were found in a midden at Rayleigh Castle, Essex, which was occupied between the eleventh and early thirteenth centuries; and bones were discovered near Ipswich beneath a piece of pottery assigned to the early twelfth century. This evidence, if correct, places the arrival of the rabbit at least a century earlier than the thirteenth, which was the period acceptable to Thompson and Worden. Sheail also mentions records of rabbits on the Scilly Isles in 1176. Lockley is also a 'Norman' supporter, but simply says it is 'generally believed' they were introduced by them, and gives no evidence. He does, however, make the interesting point that part of the equipage of the Norman conquerors was a warrener and his ferrets.

The evidence for a Roman introduction is much more scanty. Harting in *The Rabbit* says, 'We have it on the authority of the Yorkshire antiquary Whitaker that we are indebted to Roman enterprise, not only for the introduction of the rabbit, but also for the ferret which they employed to hunt it, and the Latin names for these animals, *cuniculus* and *furectus*, both of which are described by Pliny, give some colour to the assertion.' Later Harting says, 'When the Romans introduced the rabbit into Italy they introduced the custom of hunting it with ferrets; and when they carried the same animal into Britain they imported the same custom with it. The great reason for the Roman introduction of the former animal into both was the pleasure which they took in hunting it with the latter.'

Chalmers in *The Shooting-Man's England* (1936) mentions a Roman introduction, but other material he discusses at the same time obviously derives from Harting, and it is likely he is simply repeating Harting's view.

Peter Whitaker in an amusing and erudite passage in *Approach to Shooting* (1942), repeats the theory of a Roman introduction of both rabbit and ferret for sport, but the tenor of his words suggest they, too, are based on Harting. Additionally, a recent discussion I had with him indicates a change of view based on further reading.

So, for a Roman introduction there is virtually no evidence; for a Norman, the logical argument of complete silence until the eleventh century or so, followed by increasing references supporting the theory of an ever-widening population. The case for the Norman introduction is very strong, although to be fully satisfied I would need to know much more about pre-eleventh-century literature and art than I do. That minor aspect apart there remain in my mind certain reservations. The Romans were with us for some 400 years. They were a most enterprising race. We know from Pliny that their soldiers ferreted. 'It is a well-known fact that the inhabitants of the Balearic islands begged of the late Emperor Augustus the aid of a number of soldiers to prevent the too rapid increase of these animals. Ferrets are much prized on account of their hunting these animals; they are put into the burrows, with their numerous outlets, which the rabbits form, and from which circumstances they derive their name, and as the ferrets drive them out, they are taken above.' Those in charge of an army of occupation look for every means of keeping them occupied and out of mischief. Given these facts, what is more natural than that the Romans, in 400 years, should have introduced rabbits for both sport and food. Consider the behaviour of the English when they, in their turn, colonized various foreign parts. We took with us our own peculiar ways and customs, and imposed them on the assorted natives. Indeed, it would be surprizing if the Romans did not bring the rabbit to Britain.

Weight is added to the theory of a Roman introduction by a statement of Strabo's that it was a common practice to send shiploads of rabbits from Spain to Roman markets for food. (From the length of the journey and the lack of any form of refrigeration the rabbits must have travelled live.) If it was practical to transport rabbits from Spain to Italy it was equally practical to transport them to Britain. The source of supply, the means of transport and the need all existed—did nothing happen in 400 years?

Although the only case for a Roman introduction rests on logic the argument is none the less strong and I found myself wondering why, about the end of the last century, writers had swung from a Roman to a Norman introduction. (Harting, in 1898, was the last to favour the Romans.) The change apparently dates from Barret-Hamilton and Hinton's *Study of British Mammals* (1910–21), and in the absence of any new thinking, their view has been adopted by most subsequent writers. I find myself reluctant to accept the Norman introduction theory, for I would be much more convinced by positive rather than negative evidence. There is too big a question mark about the argument that because there is no recorded evidence of the rabbit before the Normans *they* must have introduced it. There must be other animals, unmentioned prior to the Normans, but no one has credited their introduction to the French. There was, I felt, a reasonable case for investigating whether the rabbit was not already well established here long before the arrival of either the Normans or the Romans. I tackled the question in three ways: by studying relevant literature; by writing to various authorities; and by letters in the sporting press appealing for information. The fact that the latter produced few replies either for or against the theory confirms that there is little generally known on the subject.

It must be appreciated that at such a distance in time it is difficult, if not impossible, to arrive at positive answers. I can but give you the available information and let you arrive at your own conclusion. The first essential is to know the dramatic extent to which the forces of nature have affected this country over many thousands of years and, for the purpose of our study, the principal influence has been what is commonly called the Ice Age. In fact, there was no single Ice Age but a sequence of periods when the ice advanced from the north, driving before it both animals and men, and then retreated. The advance of the ice coincided with a lowering of the seas and at various intervals this country was connected to the Continent by a land bridge. Given this basic information, the crux of the matter is, could the rabbit, if it was already here, have survived the extreme climatic conditions of the various ice ages, and if not, was it possible for it to have advanced across the land bridge with the Continent, as the ice retreated, before the rising seas flooded the Channel?

This is an extreme over-simplification of a complex situation and to arrive at even a possible answer we should, to quote Beirne in his *The Origin and History of the British Fauna* (1952), consider 'all known aspects of the biology, distribution and taxonomy of the animals and all available information on past climatic, vegetational and geographical changes in the British Isles'. Such a study is outside not only the scope of this book but the competence of its author and we must be content with a brief consideration. The level of the sea around us is high when compared to conditions which have existed for the greater part of the last half-million years. The British Isles are essentially part of the European mainland and sit on the shallow continental shelf which, to the west of this country, suddenly plunges to great depths. When the sea level has been low the British Isles have formed an extension of the European mainland and other areas of land, at present under the sea, have emerged. The four largest of these now drowned countries have been named by the scientists as the Cambrian, Channel, Dogger and Celtic lands with the last most important.

To read the details, in so far as we know them, of the Ice Age is to become vividly aware of the frailty of human existence. Can you imagine a world in which Arctic conditions move inexorably southwards crushing everything north of St. Albans under a vast layer of ice and sending the population of Europe fleeing south to warmer climes to compete with the indigenous populations? It would make the present turmoil in southern Africa seem like a minor disturbance at a football match. The Ice Age proper began about 600,000 years ago and although, at the moment, about one-tenth of the world is ice covered, at its peak this proportion rose to about one-third. What is technically known as the climax of the First Glacial Phase of the Last Glaciation is put at about 115,000 years ago, that of the Second Glacial Phase at about 72,000 years and the Third Glacial Phase about 22,000 years ago.

It is the last which interests us, with the question of whether the rabbit was in the country at that time, and if so whether it could have survived. I am indebted to Dr. A. J. Stuart of the Department of Zoology at the University of Cambridge who, in reply to one of my letters, confirmed the presence of the rabbit during the Ice Age with the information that 'Dr. D. F. Mayhew made a thorough study of British fossil lagomorphs and quite positively identified fossil *Oryctolagus cuniculus* (the European rabbit) from the Hoxian interglacial deposits of Swanscombe, Kent.' This is a critical item of information for our enquiry, for it confirms the presence of the rabbit thousands of years before the Romans or Normans. The question is could it have survived the ice?

It is not sufficient to investigate the climatic conditions during the various cold stages of the Ice Age and consider whether the rabbit could have survived them—the question is whether it would wish to remain in Britain, for in the absence of the Channel there was nothing to stop animals retreating before the ice. Although ice coverage ceased north of the Thames the remaining part of southern Britain suffered, during the worst period, arctic conditions. Of course, as the sea was several hundred feet lower than now the south coast must have extended much further and uncertainty exists as to the climatic conditions existing in the most southerly land areas. However, the likelihood is that the ground was in a condition of permafrost, meaning that only the top layer of soil thawed out in summer and the ground below the first foot or so was permanently frozen. My first presumption was that burrowing animals could not survive in these conditions but in correspondence with me, Dr. A. J. Sutcliffe of the Department of Palaeontology at the British Museum pointed out that in the Arctic both arctic foxes and collared lemmings live in burrows, and survive the winter. (The lemmings build moss nests in snow banks.) None the less logic suggests that as rabbits are never found on the peaks of the Scottish hills, where conditions approximate those of southern Britain during the Ice Age, they are unlikely to have remained. They would have joined the remainder of the fauna which moved south and north in response to the advance or retreat of the ice. The various authorities are by no means in agreement on whether or not the ice wiped out all our present-day common animals. Regan (1911), Reid (1916), and Charlesworth (1930) believed, in general terms, that it did. Others believe some fauna survived, but principally insects.

The weight of the evidence suggests the rabbit was pushed back or wiped out, so let us assume it was. The question which then emerges is whether, when the ice last retreated, it was able to cross the Channel land bridge before the rising seas cut this link with Europe. (The importance of this land bridge is shown by the fact that it is believed that overland migration was the main factor in the initial arrival of more than 95 per cent of British animals and the sole factor for at least 45 per cent.) Whether the rabbit beat the rising water or not depends upon many factors. Was it actually in north-west France when the climate improved? To what degree had the climate of southern England improved by the time the Channel flooded? What were the climatic conditions on what is now the bed of the Channel before it flooded, and what is the rate of colonization of rabbits? Logically I felt a crossing must have been possible, for a wide range of animals did cross. These include beetles, spiders, bees, stoats, foxes, badgers, voles and moles. Now the last four are burrowing animals, and the last two almost certainly possess a slower rate of colonization than rabbits. In other words, if they could cross the land bridge so could the rabbit. The morning after I wrote these words the post brought a letter from Dr. D. H. Maling of the Department of Geography at the University of Swansea who very kindly provided scientific confirmation. There is, he says 'abundant pollen and archaeological evidence from the southern North Sea to support this view that this was land and that the breach came about 5000 B.C.'. He then gave a range of climatic conditions which showed that the average summer temperature in south east England about 6500 B.C. was approximately 16·5 °C. From this he argued:

1. Since the breach between Britain and Europe occurred about 5000 B.C., and
2. Since the climate for 3000 years or more before that showed fluctuations which are well within the temperature tolerances which rabbits can survive at different altitudes in the U.K. today:
3. There is no reason why a wild population could not have spread into Britain from France *provided that there was a wild population there at any time before the Flandrian Transgression.*

Dr. Maling went on to explain that he did not know enough about the Old World distribution of the rabbit to offer an opinion on this latter point.

Subsequently a letter from Dr. D. F. Mayhew, whom we have already met as the identifier of the Swanscombe remains, confirmed the same general view, the relevant passage reading: 'According to West (1968) the current interglacial sea level rise appears to have cut off Britain sometime during the so-called Boreal period (pollen zone IV) around 7000–6000 B.C. At this time the climate would not have differed much from present conditions and the Channel area would have been scrubby forest rather than permafrost tundra.'

Beyond any reasonable shadow of doubt, therefore, the rabbit could have crossed if it was favourably situated on the European side at the critical time. Corlet (1966) thinks not, stating that the rabbit was formerly confined to Iberia. If he is right this certainly destroys any possibility of a natural 'land bridge' introduction, but how can his theory be reconciled with the Swanscombe, Kent, discovery? There is, however, even more positive evidence, and again I am indebted to Dr. Stuart who told me there is a single definite record of a rabbit from Thatcham, Berkshire (J. Wymer, 1962 *Proc. Prehist. Soc.*, 28: 329–61). The radio-carbon date was given as about 7500 B.C. In a subsequent letter Dr. Mayhew confirmed this, saying, 'Two bones of rabbit (definitely) with the same preservation as undoubtedly non-intrusive bones were recovered during excavations at Thatcham, Berkshire, of a mesolithic occupation site, radio-carbon dated at about 7500 B.C. (Churchill, 1962). It seems to me to be possible that the rabbit may have entered Britain at the beginning of the current interglacial, perhaps becoming extinct before the Roman/Norman invasion.'

This Thatcham discovery is of vital significance to our enquiry, for 7500 B.C. is about 9,500 years ago. At this time the climate was improving and went on improving until recent times. If rabbits were established in England at that time there is no climatic reason why they should not have survived. Dr. Mayhew suggests they might have become extinct before the Roman/Norman invasion but it is difficult to see why. If they could not only survive but thrive in the heavily populated England of the first half of this century, with the weight of science against them, they should have had few problems 10,000 years ago.

Having considered my questions and his own answers Dr. Stuart gave the opinion that 'It is therefore quite possible that the rabbit is in fact a native post-glacial member of the British fauna.'

The query may well be raised that if science can provide us with a record of the more picturesque animals that inhabited this country in the past, for example the Irish elk, how can it be vague on the humble rabbit? The reason is that the rabbit is a burrowing animal and, to quote Dr. Maling, 'the presence of rabbit bones (like badger and mouse bones) in an archaeological site has always been interpreted as modern occupation of the same site by burrowing animals. This was the only cautious and sensible interpretation which could be put on this kind of evidence and therefore such bones were discarded before modern techniques of age determination became possible.' My other correspondents make the same point.

From all the foregoing it is obvious that the rabbit could have crossed the land bridge, and apparently, some did. Whether this was an extensive and viable population which could have survived, or the remains of a few caged rabbits brought from the Continent for food, can be determined only by age determinations on rabbit bones found on widely spread archaeological sites. The technique, known as carbon-14 age determination, is expensive, and reasonably enough, has been used only to date the more exciting discoveries. I will be very pleased to hear from anyone with information in this field. I gather the Berkshire discovery is relatively new and perhaps we may now see doubts creeping into the Norman introduction theory. I hope so—I would like to think 'our' rabbits have been with us for a very long time and were not brought in, comparatively recently, by foreigners.

Mr. Daniel Haigh of Newbury suggested an interesting possibility to me. It is believed that, before the Channel filled, the Tree Men of the Continent started a regular summer trek with their herds by a high ground route, following the chalk downs between Calais and Dover, along the North Downs, the Hog's Back, the North Hants' 'Oxdrove' and across Pewsey Down to the great grazing grounds of Salisbury Plain. To take cattle on such a long journey there must have been grazing all the way, and Mr. Haigh suggests that conditions must have been favourable for the spread of rabbits. Additionally the Tree Men could have taken captive rabbits with them.

We will move now from scientific speculation to tracing the early appearances of the rabbit in history. The first mention of the rabbit I can trace is referred to by Patrick Chalmers in his *Shooting-Man's England*, who says it was known in China in 1000 B.C., and that Confucius, in the Chow Dynasty, named it among the few select creatures which the very highest gods were proud to accept in sacrifice. (Cynically one wonders whether the Chinese, a practical people, had not elected the rabbit for sacrificial purpose as a cheaper alternative than the cow or some equally large and valuable creature.) It is necessary to treat these Chinese 'rabbits' with reserve, for they may well not have been the true European wild rabbit, whose fortunes we are following. It would not be the first time an error of identity has occurred, for the 'coney of the rock', mentioned in the Authorized Version of the Bible is not, as was once thought, 'our' rabbit, but the Syrian hyrax, a small burrowing animal resembling a marmot.

Dwelling further on the subject of rabbits in China and possibly casting further doubt on Chalmers's species, there is a reference by Simpson, writing on the subject of the silver-grey wild rabbit pelt in the last century, which reads, 'Also, that until the last Chinese war they were very valuable, the skins being used for a particular class of mandarins, and commanding a high price. Since then, however, that market has been closed.' Finally, to bring the saga of Chinese rabbits up to date, I must mention an article on pet foods in the *Sunday Times* of 5 September 1976. This reported a coup by Pedigree Petfoods, who commenced importing Chinese rabbits in 1972 for conversion into Whiskas

Supermeat to the considerable betterment of the British cat diet and their own profits.

The first mention of what was almost certainly the modern European rabbit was by the Greek historian Polybius, writing of Corsica, in the second century B.C. From the works of other Greek and Latin authors it appears that the rabbit was not indigenous either in Greece or Italy, nor was it known eastward of those countries. There is no mention of it in the Bible, nor was it known to the ancient Jews. However, at this period it appears to have been very prolific in Spain. Apart from the plea of the inhabitants of the Balearic islands, mentioned earlier, rabbits also appeared on Romano-Spanish coins of the Emperor Hadrian (A.D. 117–38). Strabo, writing about 50 B.C., also confirms the abundance of the rabbit in Spain. Precisely when rabbits were introduced into Italy is not known, but they were certainly established there by A.D. 230. They appear to have become a great delicacy, and later it became the fashion to eat the embryos on fast-days. The rabbit appears to have been domesticated by the first century B.C., and later, the Roman scholar Varro wrote a detailed description of the walled enclosures (leporaria), in which they were kept—a development which, more than a thousand years later, was to make its impact on English agriculture.

In this country rabbits were, until comparatively recently, known as coneys, the name rabbit being reserved for the young. In turn coney comes from the Latin *cuniculus*, which also signifies an underground passage, and from which all the main European names for the rabbit are derived. Thus Italian *coniglio*; Spanish *conejo*; Portuguese *coelho*; Belgian *konin*; Danish and Swedish *koning*; German *kaninchen*; Old French *connin*; Welsh *cwningen* and the Old English *conyng* and *coney*. The *Promptorium Parvulorum* (1440) mentions 'Rabet, a yonge conye', and Russell's *Book of Nurture* (1424) mentions 'rabbettes'.

Harting, in an interesting passage, says that an alternative name for the rabbit, used in hunting circles, was *riote*, and the behaviour of hounds when they encountered one explains the origin of the phrase 'to run riot'. He quotes an old MS in the Bodleian Library in which the huntsman is directed to shout, at the appropriate time, 'war ryote war! for noon other wylde beest yn Ingelande is called *ryote* saf the conyng alonly.'

The part of the rabbit in the countryside, although by no means insignificant, has always been unobtrusive, and the records that exist of it through the ages are mainly incidental—minor details on a wide canvas. We know they existed in Wales in the thirteenth century, although they failed to spread much beyond the coastal areas before the end of the eighteenth century. They were also in Ireland by the thirteenth century and by the fourteenth century skins were being exported. Sheail mentions the existence of a small number of medieval drawings and sketches in which either rabbits or hares, it is difficult to distinguish which appear. One, dated 1245, is in the Hampshire Record Office, and another, in which the subjects are clearly rabbits, is a painting at Longthorpe Tower, near Peterborough, dating from the fourteenth century.

Understandably, many of the old records relate to the use of the rabbit as food. In 1270, 200 rabbits were supplied for the feast of St. Edward, celebrated by the King at Westminster; Queen Anne appears to have been very fond of rabbit tart; and 'The Noble Boke of Cookry for a Prynce's Houseolde or any other estately houseolde' recommends the use of rabbits in the cooler months. The rabbit must have been a godsend to the chief cook at an old-time feast, faced with the large numbers of guests and the greater problems of his day in both obtaining and storing food. What, for example, would the alternative have been at the feast for the installation of the Archbishop of York in 1467 had not 4,000 rabbits been available? Not that rabbits were necessarily cheap. The house records of Lord Howard show that early in the seventeenth century, rabbits cost about 8d a couple; hares about 6d; partridges about 4d and grouse 3d–5d. Harting makes the good point that, considering the extent to which people of this period depended upon the rabbit for food, it is strange how frequently they used the inferior method of baking. Having no fat the rabbit, to eat at its best, must be liberally basted. One alternative to roasting was to 'Smyt them in small pieces and sethe them in good brothe put them to mynced onyons and grece and drawe a liour of brown bred and blod and seison it with venygar and cast in pouder and salt and serve it.'

The growing need for food gave extra incentive to the spread of warrens in this country; a major development in the history of the rabbit which warrants mentioning in some detail. It is important to distinguish between rabbit warrens and what was known as a free warren. The latter was merely a sporting right over an area of land, granted by the Crown, and was restricted to those creatures which could be taken by a large hawk; that is the hare, rabbit, pheasant and partridge. (In 1380 the Bishop of Winchester sued Sir John Gifford and his men for entering a warren without licence.) A true rabbit warren was land set aside for the specific purpose of breeding rabbits which, although confined within the boundaries of the warren, otherwise lived in a wild state.

Lockley in *The Private Life of the Rabbit* claims that one of his fields is laid out in a manner typical of a twelfth century-Norman warren, but the first warren mentioned by Sheail was in 1253. This was at Farnham, Surrey, and was still functioning in 1376, when rabbits were sold at 2½d each. The Norman term for a warren was coneygarth, and alternatives were coney-warren and conigree. At a time when agricultural knowledge and machinery were primitive warrening was a sensible and popular form of land use, and Sheail's book contains a map of England showing the numerous place-names in which the word warren appears. Considering the many warrens that existed, the actual records throughout the fourteenth, fifteenth and sixteenth centuries appear scanty; no doubt because, like so many aspects of life, warrens were so common that no special comment was needed. In 1788 William Marshall gave a detailed description of two warrens at Driffield in Yorkshire, but the stimulus was not the existence of anything so common as a warren but their tendency to flood in heavy rain, causing litters of young rabbits to float to the surface. Other reports also owe their existence to special circumstances; a report of an English raiding party to the Isle of Moy in Lincolnshire in the sixteenth century said, 'the warrens were completely destroyed'. And in the eighteenth century, in Lincolnshire, rabbits caused so much damage that local people 'ruined the warrens'.

A clue to the one-time existence of a warren is often given by evidence of old earthworks. It was common to construct mounds or banks to provide other ground for burrowing than purely flat fields. These earthworks varied from simple mounds, some six feet (1·8 m) high and the same in diameter, to banks between parallel ditches, a hundred yards (91 m) or more in length. In establishing a new warren it was necessary to provide not only banks but preliminary holes. Sheail reports the following entry in the accounts for the production of a new warren at Hampton Court for Henry VIII: 'To Robert Bing, of the Wyke smythe, for a great long nagre [auger] of irne, to make and bore cony holes within the kynges beries new made for blake conyes in the warren.' And Lord Howard's records had an entry for 5th April 1633 for 'makinge cunnie burrows in the warren, xvjs' (sixteen shillings).

Until the sixteenth century most warrens were unenclosed, with the rabbits free to come, or more usually go, as they pleased, but during the next two centuries the practice of surrounding the warrens with some form of rabbit-proof walling developed. Stone and wood were sometimes used for the fence, but the most common method was usually a six-foot (1·8 m) high wall, built of grass sods, and capped with furze, blackthorn or reeds. When conditions in the warren were reasonable this relatively un-rabbit-proof barrier sufficed, but when the population density was high, or food scarce, the warreners had a heavy task in keeping the wall repaired. As an example of the problem the perimeter of the Thetford warren was eight miles.

The invention of wire netting greatly eased the problem of containment for warreners, and by the end of the nineteenth century was the standard means of fencing. Both Simpson and Harting give precise details on fence construction, but while both agree over a six-inch (15 cm) horizontal flap at top and bottom, Simpson is far more of an optimist over height. While Harting recommends four feet (1·2 m), Simpson is content with three feet (0·9 m) which, he says 'is a formidable obstruction to poachers, and an almost complete safeguard against foxes, which do not like to jump even a low fence with no top to it to speak of, and surrounded by a barbed wire'. I can only comment that the athletic performance of both foxes and poachers appears to have improved substantially since Simpson's time.

For anyone interested in the history and practice of warrens Simpson's book is required reading. *The Wild Rabbit in a New Aspect or Rabbit-Warrens that Pay* is a record of experiments in warren improvement carried out on the estate of the Earl of

Wharncliffe, and the first edition was published in 1895. Simpson was a 'Wood-agent, etc.' and obviously a practical man with an enquiring and business-like mind. One of his main arguments was that maintaining a large head of rabbits on a small area of land gradually impoverished it, and if a warren was to remain productive the land required regular dressing with lime and manure. By this means he succeeded in feeding approximately 100 rabbits per acre (0·4 h), which makes an interesting comparison with Lockley's figure of 32 per acre. The wisdom of this practice is underlined by a warrener reporting to a Select Committee in 1872. When asked why the birth-rate on his warren was low, he replied that the rabbits 'never had a honeymoon'—in other words they never enjoyed rich feeding. Simpson's near contemporary, Harting, obviously thought highly of his ideas and work and draws extensively on his views in his own chapter on warrens, at one point saying, 'This excellent advice of Mr. Simpson'.

The great value, both in quantity and financial terms, of the food produced by the warrens can be seen from the occasional statistics that occur in past records. In the early years of the nineteenth century the *Agricultural Survey of Lincolnshire* reported that of the eighteen miles (28·9 km) of countryside lying between Louth and Caistor, no less than ten (16 km) were warrens. (The same source reported that the average price paid for the rabbits was £10 per hundred, which is 10p each, or 2s in the currency of the time and, also, the one that many of us still use in assessing value. This price, when considered in the light of the wages of the period, seems very high, a view confirmed by a letter in *The Field* of 14 March 1896, very nearly a century later. This said, 'Trapped or snared rabbits should realise, say, 2s 9d a couple; shot ones 2s 8d a couple; taking out, of course, any badly shot, and sending only good sound rabbits to market.' A Mr. Grant of Withgal is reported to have had a warren of 1,000 acres, with an annual kill of 10,000. Even allowing for the wages of his warreners this £1,000 per annum must have left him very comfortably off, although Simpson felt that, using his methods, the bag should have been increased fivefold.) By the ninteeenth century the number of warrens was decreasing, but even so, at the vast Thetford warren, between the seasons of 1855–6 and 1861–2, there was an average of 28,886 rabbits killed each year.

There were several reasons for the gradual disappearance of the warrens, but the most forceful was the improvement of agricultural knowledge and techniques, which made it possible to grow valuable crops on marginal land, which had previously yielded a better return from rabbits. The counter-argument was, in fact, the essence of Simpson's book, which appeared at the end of the last century when warrens were becoming scarce. Simpson claimed that it was unrealistic to compare land which had been carefully husbanded and used for crop growing with land, completely neglected, used for raising rabbits. A true comparison could only be made if the warrens were also managed with the same care and this done, Simpson claimed rabbits were more profitable than corn or any other crop. In the event no one listened and the warrens died. Quite how many there were at the peak we will never know, for the evidence is too fragmentary. We do know, however, that their passing brought great changes to the appearance of large areas of the countryside. It was said that before the improvements all that part of Norfolk between Holkham and Houghton was a wild sheep walk. A good example was the Sandringham Heath Warren which, in 1750, was broken up to take crops of corn and turnips. Wordwell Warren went in 1853, but the most telling piece of evidence came from Mr. C. S. Reid giving evidence to a Select Committee of the House of Commons. He could remember, he said, between 15,000 to 20,000 acres (6,000–8,000 h) of rabbit warrens in Norfolk, but at the time of speaking, 1873, only 5,000 to 6,000 acres (2,000–2,400 h) remained.

The passing of the Ground Game Act in 1880 put further pressure on the warrens, for it gave to tenants the right to kill rabbits on their land. Although the main incentive was crop protection, farmers quickly found the rabbits provided an additional source of income, which cost them virtually nothing to produce. This home competition was further supplemented by the increasing importance of rabbit skins, for the value of a rabbit was not limited to the meat alone. A Select Committee found that in the 1860s, in the peak four months of the year, 8,000 people were employed in the collection, dyeing and preparation of the skins and wools. But shortly after this report, in 1869, Australia began to export skins to England. By 1889, the value of Australian skins arriving here had grown to £341,733, and by 1903 it had more than doubled to £723,881.

No part of the rabbit was wasted. The furriers sold their waste to the milliners who used it for stuffing beds and bolsters. And the other trimmings of the furriers, spoilt skins, ears, tails, legs, etc., were used by farmers as manure. (A Board of Agriculture *Report* of 1809 remarked upon a fine crop of potatoes grown at Godstone on furriers' clippings.)

And so, slowly, the warrens died out, but the best took a long time to go. On my journeys to shoot in Norfolk I pass along the boundary of the vast Lakenheath aerodrome in Suffolk. Not so many years ago this was the Lakenheath Warren on that most famous sporting estate, Elveden, the details of which have been permanently recorded by Tommy Turner in his *Memoirs of a Gamekeeper* (1954). He recalls that the banks enclosing the warren were four and a half feet high and surmounted with gorse faggots, specially cut and laid with the prickly part facing inward. At one time there were thirty warreners employed and 'In the first full season after the first World War 81,000 rabbits were killed by shooting, ferreting, trapping and by netting at night, and in the next two seasons 128,856 and 123,928.' Even after the Second World War, when the estate was attempting to eliminate rabbits rather than harvest them, they were still killing some 50,000 a year, although Turner wrote, 'but in this last year, 1952–53, the number was down to 19,528'. Little did he suspect the carnage shortly to come.

Before we leave warrens it is interesting to look at the methods by which the warreners overcame the practical problem of catching large numbers of rabbits, and this during the hard weather of the 'killing season', which ran from October to February. Ferreting was, of course, a common method and Turner reckoned a good man would kill two or three dozen in a day, although mentioning two men who took well over one hundred.

Netting was very popular, as it left the rabbits unmarked, and Harting gave detailed descriptions of 'fold-nets' and 'spring-nets'. But the greatest execution was done by the old 'tipe' or tip-trap, with which it was possible to take five or six hundred rabbits in a night. The device was simple, effective and allowed the warrener to release unharmed both small rabbits to grow bigger and does to achieve the desired balance of sexes. (Ideally one buck to six or seven does; which was hard on the surplus bucks but made for a merry, if tiring life for the fortunate surviving males.) In operation the device was a cistern or tank, buried to ground level, and with a horizontal lid balanced on a central pin. The cistern was sited at, or rather below, a busy thoroughfare, and the lid bolted firmly to allow a safe crossing until the warrener chose to begin catching.

Simpson, true to form, was not content with this and devised a 'rabbit-trap-fence', to the description of which he devotes an entire chapter. In brief it consisted of two parallel wire fences, one laid flat, along the edge of the covert. When the rabbits emerged to feed they would walk over the flat fence, be stopped by the second, feed resignedly on the grass they could reach, and when sufficient numbers had accumulated, operators would haul the flat fence upright by distant wires and trap the rabbits in between.

This is, necessarily, a brief summary of warrens. I only wish I had the space, the time and the material to study them in more detail, and to unravel the part they played in the history of the English countryside. We know little of the life of the warreners; their training and skills; the problems of transporting to market and storing rabbits in the days before refrigeration. There are many interesting questions to ask and perhaps answer.

Following the growth and decline of warrens has led us too rapidly from the thirteenth to the twentieth century, missing many interesting items en route. As I noted earlier very few people wrote specifically about rabbits—they were too commonplace to justify special mention—it is the incidental references which spotlight our subject. Marketing records are a good example. We know that in 1274, Lundy Isle, in the Bristol Channel, sent 2,000 skins to the mainland, and over 500 years later, in 1787, was still exporting the same quantity. The *Ipswich Journal* of 1755 carried an advertisement inviting farmers to bring their rabbit carcases to Newmarket in lots of twelve dozen. And H. E. Strickland, writing in 1812, describes how the hucksters of Yorkshire played a leading part in purchasing rabbits from local warrens and transporting them to the large towns. The rabbits were strung on rods on covered carts, sometimes with as many as 600–800 couple to each cart. Meat went to York, Hull, Leeds,

Bradford and Halifax and skins to the furriers at Stamford Bridge and Malton. The river Trent carried large numbers of rabbits from the warrens of Lincolnshire to Hull, and in 1835 Sir George Head described the transfer of rabbit carcases from the river transport to the carts: 'they are strung by the legs on poles, and put into carts; each cart contains ten poles, each pole carries a couple of score of rabbits, making four hundred for a cart-load.' About this time a London poultry salesman reported to a Select Committee of 1828 that each November morning he received on contract, from mainly Norfolk warrens, 200 *dozen* rabbits.

The numbers of rabbits passing down the throats of the English each year during this period can only be guessed at, but the total must have been prodigious. I refer specifically to English throats as consumption of rabbits was localized until comparatively recently. It appears to have been common near Edinburgh from the sixteenth century but, apart from some islands and coastal areas, was rare in the remainder of Scotland until the early nineteenth century. We know that there were established warrens in East Lothian and Heddington before the 1840s, for they supplied rabbits to Edinburgh, but after the construction of the railway the supply went to the presumably more lucrative market of Newcastle. There were certainly enough rabbits in Scotland by the seventeenth century for them to be deemed worthy of legislation for, at that time, the right to kill game was vested in the landlord and, by an Act of 1621 only the owners of more than one ploughgate of land (that is 130 imperial acres) could kill game. The Board of Agriculture reports of around 1800 do not mention rabbits at all in Ross and Cromarty and suggest there were not more than one hundred in Aberdeenshire.

These same reports are also useful in forming a picture of rabbit densities in England at that time, suggesting very large numbers in the warrens of Norfolk, Suffolk, Lincolnshire and Nottinghamshire; a few warrens only in Huntingdonshire and Buckinghamshire, and a patchy situation is reported with wild rabbits in other areas. There were, for example, a lot in Middlesex, a few in Surrey and 'average' numbers in Cambridgeshire. Rabbits were also reported in Sussex, Kent, Dorset and Shropshire. Surprisingly, the only deliberate attempt to forecast the rabbit population of England before the beginning of the present century was made as far back as the 1690s by Gregory King in his *Natural and Political Observations* (1696). Obviously he had only the most limited data available and his conclusions can be no more than informed guesswork, but, in the absence of any other information, he casts a bright light into a dark corner. King estimated the rabbit stock at 1,000,000 and the yearly 'bred or increase' at 2,000,000. The hare population he estimated at only 24,000 and sheep at no less than 11,000,000. A population of only 1,000,000 for the entire country suggests that rabbits, at that time, were not very common, except in certain restricted areas. But their numbers were probably higher than they had been at any time since their introduction, and in the eighteenth century there began an increase which can only be described as dramatic. By the 1930s it was estimated that the British rabbit population was no less than fifty million and just before myxomatosis struck in 1953, forecasts varied between sixty and one hundred million.

Why? What factors not only permitted but encouraged such a startling growth? As always when peering into the past we cannot be sure but, almost certainly, two changes in the rabbit's environment, both brought about by man, were responsible. The first, and more obvious, was the change in agricultural methods which provided more and better food. Not long ago I had cause to study the natural history of the woodpigeon and was struck by the absolute relationship between the food supply and pigeon numbers. It was the change in agricultural practices which brought about both the great post-war increase in pigeon numbers—principally due to under-sowing leys—and the recent fall—owing to the increased tendency to burn stubbles and plough immediately after harvest. So it was with the rabbit. Just as pigeons had once starved in the bare countryside of February, March and April, so the rabbit numbers were limited by minimal food supplies. But the seventeenth and eighteenth centuries saw a steady growth in the use of winter fodder crops, which provided an excellent and reliable source of rabbit food. Sheail takes the logic further, arguing that winter fodder meant many more sheep; more sheep meant more manure; more manure meant more fertilized cropland, which meant more cultivation; more winter food; more sheep; and so on, while all the time the rabbits benefited and multiplied. He also reasons that the technique of managing water-meadows, where sheep could be pastured three weeks earlier, also reduced the 'hungry gap' in the year. This was also a period when many new hedges were planted, providing ideal homes for rabbits on the very edge of their dining tables.

The second change was the rise of interest in sporting shooting. Through the first half of the seventeenth century most shooting was more concerned with procuring food than sport, a fact well illustrated by the title of Gervase Markham's book, published in 1621 and entitled *Hunger's Prevention, Or The Whole Art of Fowling by Water and Land*, but with the restoration of the monarchy in 1660, Charles II and his followers brought back from France a liking for the new sport of shooting flying birds. By 1686, Richard Blome's *The Gentlemans Recreation*, dealt at length with the art, and by the start of the eighteenth century the landed gentry of England were firmly wedded to the sport. At first shooting men were content with whatever quarry God provided, but as the pressure on finite numbers of birds and animals increased men began to turn their minds to helping nature. Soon the gamekeeper entered the scene, to stand alongside the long established warrener, and rapidly evolved the principle of killing everything harmful to pheasants and partridges. Down came the numbers of what they called vermin and our more enlightened age calls predators, and in particular, stoats, weasels, foxes, rats and badly behaved cats. With natural enemies greatly thinned and food not only present in greater quantity but, more important, available the year round, the rabbits responded magnificently.

Too magnificently for some, and in particular the unfortunate tenant farmers who were not, in law, permitted to kill rabbits and had to stand by and watch them eating their crops. In many cases the increase of rabbit numbers occurred not by default but design, for rabbit shooting was a sport greatly favoured by the landlords or shooting tenants. Sheail quotes many instances of rabbit damage in the 1800s; for example, the farmer who complained to a Select Committee in 1845 that while his rent was £370 per annum he reckoned to lose another £180–200 a year through rabbit damage. He even reports one man committing suicide whilst crying, 'Rabbits have killed me', and a Mrs. Cresswell was so incensed as to complain about the damage done by 'Royal Guns' on her farm at Sandringham. There was, she said, a procession of Guns, loaders, servants and spectators walking through the crops.

By the middle of the nineteenth century the situation had become so serious that pressure to alter or remove the Game Laws (which allowed landlords to forbid tenants to kill rabbits) became intense. An Anti-Game Law League was formed and campaigned extensively for change, while some tenant farmers openly encouraged poaching on their ground, always provided, of course, that rabbits were the prime target. An 1879 issue of *Farming* contained a satirical attack on landlords, supposedly written by 'Jeremiah Mangoldwurzle', and set within the framework of a fictitious meeting of the Blankshire landowners in The Rabbit Rampant Inn, Coneyboro. At this various speakers praised the rabbit, 'The Landlords' Perquisite', pointing out that unlike tenants, they never sought repairs to their buildings. Rabbits, one speaker was reported to say, were preferable to tenants and he 'meant to pweserve them much more wigorously'. Tenants should be forbidden to carry guns under the pretence of shooting vermin. 'It was putting temptation in their way to allow them guns among a flock of wabbits. Pwetending to shoot wooks indeed!'

Shortly after this one of the most important items of legislation to affect the status of the rabbit became law, to wit the Ground Game Act of 1880. I deal with the rabbit and the law in some detail in the chapter on poaching, so will only outline here the principle of this important Act. The main provision was to give to every occupier of land an inalienable right to kill ground game. It did not affect the protection enjoyed by winged game, nor place the right to kill rabbits and hares with either tenant or landlord. Both could pursue rabbits and hares, and sometimes both did, to the irritation of the principals and the amusement of onlookers. Of course, the Act was far more complex than the simple statement above, but the great outstanding change was that rabbit control no longer depended on the whim of the landlord. Nor was the tenant's power to kill rabbits restricted to him in person, for he could authorize, in writing, another person to do the job within certain reasonable limitations. Many landlords who had valued their rabbits either for sport or money, feared for their survival under the new and vigorous attack of the tenants, but the effect was much less dramatic. Where the degree of nuisance was so high as to stimulate the tenants into serious and sustained measures, population restrictions were achieved, but elsewhere the rabbits not only survived but multiplied and extended their range. The proof of this statement may be found in many references to rabbit numbers within a decade or so of 1880. For example, Simpson says, 'It is nothing unusual in large towns to see hundreds suspended in front of one shop at a time, nearly the whole of which must be sold within a short while if they are to be sold at all.' Even more telling are the old bag records. Lloyd Price, author of *Rabbits for Profit and Rabbits for Powder* (1884), cited bags of 1,650, 1,850 and 2,500, all in single days. These impressive totals were later knocked into insignificance by single day shoots on his ground at Rhiwlas, North Wales. In 1883 (just three years, be it noted, after The Ground Game Act), 3,684 rabbits were killed, and in 1885 the incredible total of 5,086 was reached. Imagine the sheer physical problems posed by just cleaning and transporting the corpses. On this latter occasion 920 were shot by Lord de Grey. (It is necessary to treat these large figures with a certain reserve, for it is likely that, as with good fish, the passage of time does nothing to diminish them. The first figures of 1,650, 1,850 and 2,500 are too neatly rounded to be strictly accurate. It is highly unlikely that the men who did the killing did the counting and the head keeper, stepping wearily up to the big house to report the bag, and with the tip well in mind, would not err on the conservative side. Even the 5,086 of 1885 had grown to 5,096 by the time it reached the pages of Teasdale-Buckell's *The Complete Shot.*) Lord de Grey's 920 is believed to be the best day's bag of rabbits by a single Gun. Next comes Sir Victor Brooke, at Colebrook, Co. Fermanagh, who, also in 1885, shot 740. He is reported to have fired exactly 1,000 cartridges, but lacked the fortitude of Lord de Grey for he fired from his right shoulder for half the day and his left for the remainder. Shooting within warrens, although strictly speaking outside the point I am trying to make, also produced large bags. On 19 November 1894 Mr. Charles Eley and a friend, shooting in a warren of only forty acres, killed 900 rabbits—or so it was reported in *The Field* shortly after. Note once again the round figure of 900. (Harting shares my slightly sceptical approach to the reported deeds of his fellows. Observe my italics in the following passage from his book: 'It was reported in *The Field* of 9th September, 1893. Mr. W. C. Pickering, of Rehwl House, Mostyn, Flintshire, shooting with one of the handy little rifles above referred to, fired at three rabbits in line and killed them all; and strange to say, on a subsequent occasion, *so he said*, he repeated the performance.')

Jobbing back in time, a day on Lord Stamford's Bradygate estate in December 1861 when 3,333 rabbits were killed by 13 Guns is worthy of mention, not because of the bag—formidable though it is, but because the weapons were all muzzle-loaders.

Nowadays we pay little regard to any but the most blatant variations of the rabbit's colouring but in the eighteenth century, and into the beginning of the nineteenth, the value of the fur varied considerably with the colour and some warrens specialized in the more sought after 'silver grey'. Simpson reported that some silver-grey warrens were still operating when he wrote (late nineteenth century) and sought from one owner, Captain Vyner of Askrigg, North Yorkshire, an explanation of the origin of this colour form. The Captain replied, 'Sir Walter Raleigh brought the silver-grey rabbits to Nappa warren at Askrigg and that the rabbits were turned down in a sixty acre warren, surrounded by a wall, and have been there ever since.' Simpson also reported an active silver-grey warren in Norfolk, on the estate of Lord Walsingham (a name that will ring an instant bell in the minds of all shooting men). The other three colours commonly traded in were the common grey, the wild black rabbit, and the sandy; the latter being of poorer quality and, reputedly, fetching only half price of the common grey. The skins, incidentally, were not always sold complete. Milliners frequently made hats from rabbit fur, separated from the skin and dressed to look like beaver, and the art of paring the fur from the skin was known to have been practised from early times. The skin was dampened, then hung with a heavy weight to keep it taut, the fur then being shaved from the skin with a sharp knife. A rabbit, in the killing season, produced about an ounce of fur or wool, and it was separated for sale according to the part of the skin from which it was taken. In 1800 wool from the back fetched 20s a lb., from the breach 18s, from the belly and throat and the head 14s. Tails fetched 12s a lb.

We have now reached the closing years of the nineteenth century and stand poised to enter our own. Before doing so we will look at the story of the rabbit in Australia; an awe-inspiring example of the capacity of rabbits to expand and multiply in favourable conditions. The first rabbits were introduced into Australia in 1787 and more followed in 1791, but it is not believed these survived. The honour of the Australian conquest goes to just twenty-four wild British rabbits sent to Barwon Park in the State of Victoria in 1859. In the century that followed they spread, in their millions, over two-thirds of the Continent, existing happily in semi-desert areas with rainfalls of less than seven inches (17 cm) a year to wet areas with up to seventy-five inches (190 cm). Once the Australians awoke to the threat of this self-imposed and gentle looking creature, they went to enormous lengths to control it, spending in the process hundreds of millions of pounds. The most imaginative plan was to stop the invasion by the erection of the Great Barrier Fences. These ran north and south across thousands of miles through New South Wales, Queensland and Western Australia, and were intended to stop the western spread of the rabbit. The longest, completed in 1907, took five years to build and ran from Hopetown on the south coast to Eighty Mile Beach on the north. Even before the erection of the fences was completed rabbits were to be seen on both sides, and so, like a retreating army digging ever-new front line trenches, new fences were begun. Although the open nature of the terrain avoided the problems, both physical and of ownership, which would have been encountered in England, the problems of maintenance and constantly stopping newly dug holes were immense. Once the rabbits had clearly breached the defences, incentive died and the fences were left to rot. Not only the fences but every other method of control failed. Failure is, perhaps, too strong a word, for many millions of rabbits were killed and a measure of control achieved, but at no time was there any prospect of extermination, even over limited areas. Poisoning was carried out on a massive scale, with fruit and vegetables dusted with strychnine, phosphorus or arsenic. These were often laid mechanically in a freshly ploughed furrow. In dry areas poisoning water holes was very successful with kills of as many as a hundred thousand in a single night. More eccentric methods were tried, including the Rodier Method. This involved capturing as many rabbits as possible in an area and then killing the does and releasing all the bucks, in the belief that the few surviving does would not survive the sexual onslaught of so many males. The Method appears to have greatly underestimated the amorous ability of female rabbits, or perhaps their less favoured sisters around the periphery came in to enjoy the fun, for it was eventually abandoned. In 1887 the government of New South Wales offered £25,000 for the eradication of the colony's rabbits, a considerable fortune which brought a response from Louis Pasteur. Unknowingly foreseeing myxomatosis he proposed introducing a fatal contagion which would spread throughout the whole rabbit population, and suggested the chicken cholera bacillus, *Pasteurella septica*. The strength of his reputation led to the proposal being seriously considered but, not unnaturally, there was unease at introducing cholera and, eventually, the quarantine authorities prohibited the introduction.

More conventional methods were tried, including the importation of foxes, although the wish to take the sport of fox hunting to the new Continent may have been at least as powerful a factor as the desire to kill rabbits. In the event the fox emulated the rabbit and is now a pest in some areas. Another interesting example of Australian attempts to control rabbits by importing their natural enemies arises from a passage in Noel Sedgwick's *Wildfowling and Rough Shooting* (1950), 'Stoats, like ferrets, are thirsty little creatures, and I well remember when we were catching stoats to be sent out to Australia we were told that at least one consignment had died on board ship because those in charge did not realize that they needed plenty of water.'

One of the problems of rabbit control has always been that those who are paid to do the controlling have a natural reluctance to exterminate the source of their income; which leads to an amusing story from New Zealand in 1894. A bounty scheme was introduced whereby 2d was paid for each rabbit tail handed in. No great knowledge of countrymen is needed to guess that, before long, tail-less wild rabbits were a common sight.

No man invented myxomatosis—it was a naturally occurring virus, but it was the urgent need to control the Australian rabbits which led to the discovery of how to spread it among wild rabbits.

The detail must await the chapter on the disease but the effect has altered the entire agricultural picture of Australia. During the first year of major impact, 1951–2, some areas saw 'kill' rates of the order of 99·5 per cent, and it is estimated that in 1952–3 the value of rural production increased by about £50,000,000.

But we progress too far and must return to England at the turn of the century. Snippets of interesting information may be gleaned from various sources. Simpson tells us, for example, that at this time a rabbit of fair size and condition would fetch 1s to 1s 3d, but that, if one overcame any scruples against the sport, supplying live ones for coursing would fetch 4s to 5s per couple.

Up to this time the value and usefulness of wild rabbits was determined by their distance from large centres of population, for the distance they could be transported before deteriorating was often very limited by the available transport. Many travelled by sea, and Harting reports, 'There was a time, in the period of the carrier's cart and the sailing smack, when the Scotch servants and retainers struck against the rabbits, as they did against the monotony of salmon and sea-trout.' (I, too, could mutiny against salmon, but sea-trout—never!) The railways, of course, made rabbits a common food of the working classes of the great industrial towns. It is also from Harting that I pluck this pointer to the future, 'With the perfection of refrigerating chambers, the importation from Australia and New Zealand has been increasing fast.'

Tommy Turner's *Memoirs of a Gamekeeper* provides a feast of information, too much, indeed, to serve in detail, but worthy of study, not only for its rabbit content but because of the simple but impressive picture it provides of the workings of a great sporting estate unconsciously moving, for political reasons, into the close of an era. I mentioned earlier the huge bags achieved on the Elveden estate (growing from 6,778 in 1894–5, to 81,000 in 1946–7), but the book does more than record sheer numbers—it shows the part the rabbit played in the countryside. One interesting item confirms the old practice of feeding game birds on rabbit, and Turner mentions rearing partridges on a mixture that included rice, eggs and chopped rabbit. Further evidence comes in the Badminton book on *Shooting* (by Walsingham and Payne-Gallwey, 1889), which treats the practice of using chopped rabbit to feed pheasants as commonplace. Turner mentions that in the Second World War rabbits were sold at a controlled price of 9d a lb. During the war years the estate was taken over by the army and much of the ground taken for exercises. Tanks were continually driven over the warrens and Turner records that, as time went on, the rabbits disappeared. He writes as if the fact surprises him, but after giving the opinion that there were several causes for the migration, concludes that the tanks were the main cause. I agree! With the end of the war and the departure of the tanks, the rabbits reappeared, giving bags of: 1945–6, 15,496; 1946–7, 11,350; 1947–8, 14,246.

I mentioned earlier the numbers of factories that once existed to utilize the rabbit in various ways. Turner said there were two at Brandon and reported one was still operating when he wrote (1954), being chiefly concerned with making fur hats. The felt hat, or bowler, was covered with shellac and then spun round at great speed while rabbit fur was blown onto it, producing a soft glossy finish.

It was not only on the Elveden estate that rabbit numbers increased during the first half of the present century. By the late 1930s their numbers were estimated at about fifty million, which was four times the head of sheep. Sedgwick reported a House of Lords debate in which the 1938 consumption of home-killed rabbits was put at no less than forty-four million, weighing 800,000 cwt. (40,640 t). (These were divided as to seven million killed in Scotland and thirty-seven million in England and Wales.) By the beginning of the fifties the official pre-myxomatosis estimate of the rabbit population was sixty to one hundred million, but Thompson and Worden have reservations, suggesting the population in the spring and summer months was likely to have exceeded the hundred million mark. Interestingly, although the rabbit population in the early fifties was nearly double that of the late thirties, the number passing through dealers' hands was down, at only some forty million. The explanation, no doubt, was the much increased standard of living and the availability of relatively cheap imported beef, lamb and other meat.

Further useful statistics can be gleaned from the Department of Animal Health, Aberystwyth, who reported the weights of rabbits sent from the railway stations of three Welsh counties in

1948 totalled 3,320 tons (3,373 t), which represented some four and a half million rabbits. In the same year over 800 tons (813 t) were sent from both Devon and Cornwall. Meanwhile the imports of rabbits were growing steadily. Sedgwick put the 1938 figure at less than 10,000 tons (10,160 t), but his House of Lords debate put the 1947 imports at 21,250 tons (21,590 t). Yet, only a year later, Thompson and Worden report imports as 32,000 tons (32,512 t).

We have followed, albeit intermittently, the history of the rabbit through the centuries. At the moment at which we leave it, to pass on to a consideration of its arch-enemy the ferret, it appears impregnable in the niche it has carved for itself in the ecology of the countryside. No one could anticipate the terrible disaster about to strike.

CHAPTER TWO

The Mystery and History of the Ferret

Any detailed consideration of the ferret must immediately raise the interesting question of what it is and where it came from, and none of my research for this book led me down more fascinating lines of enquiry. In fact very few people have any firm evidence of the origin of the ferret, as is obvious from the correspondence when the subject makes one of its occasional appearances in the sporting press. The latest, at the moment of writing, occurred in the *Shooting Times and Country Magazine* in 1975, and various suggestions ranged from 'the Russian or Steppe polecat' to introduction from North Africa or, more specifically, Morocco.

There are two separate pathways to the truth—either by specific references in earlier literature or by scientific logic. Whilst the latter is the more convincing the former is more interesting, so I will give it priority.

Modern authors have nothing new to say on the subject and content themselves with repeating the views of earlier writers (sometimes giving credit to their source and sometimes not). It is to the prolific writers of the last century, and the early years of this, that we must look for enlightenment, but we are not helped by comparing Harting in *The Rabbit*, who says the ferret is merely a domesticated polecat, with Nicholas Everitt in *Ferrets*, who was emphatic that it was not. 'Some naturalists', he wrote in 1897, 'have expressed it as their opinion that the ferret and the polecat are one and the same animal, and the variety in colour and size is only a peculiarity. Nowadays all doubts on this point seem to be cleared up and the distinction is marked.' Having said what a ferret was not there was an obligation on Everitt to say what it was and, after searching the dictionaries to no avail, he stated that it was a native of Africa, subsequently introduced into Europe. By 'native' he inferred that it existed in a wild state in Africa and this is confirmed by an earlier comment that 'ferrets are not found *feræ naturæ* in the British Isles and must be acclimatized and domesticated.' To support his belief Everitt gave separate descriptions of the ferret and the polecat but these showed no real distinction other than size. For example, the body of the ferret is described as 'long and thin' and that of the polecat as 'elongated, slender, and very flexible'.

Barkley, writing just a year earlier in 1896, supports Everitt, saying ferrets are not natives of Great Britain and were imported from Morocco. However, he gives no reference and cannot be granted the authority of Harting who quotes the ancient author Strabo, writing about 50 B.C. on the problems caused by an abundance of rabbits in Spain. 'Many ways of hunting had been devised', he wrote, 'amongst others by wild weasels from Africa, trained for the purpose. Having muzzled these they turn them into the holes, where they either drag out the animals they find there with their claws, or compel them to fly to the surface, where they are taken by people standing by for that purpose.' Now here we have a real gem of a clue—a positive factual statement from the past, which by its coupled reference to muzzling and bolting rabbits can only apply to ferreting as we know it.

So we have now established a well-founded claim for the ferret having originated as a naturally occurring wild animal of Africa, subsequently introduced into Britain. Who would have introduced it? Certainly if the Romans introduced the rabbit, or if it was here before their arrival, then they would also have brought the ferret, for, in addition to Strabo, there is ample evidence to show they were familiar with ferrets and their uses. Pliny also described the ferret (which has the Latin name of *furectus*). When mentioning the famine caused in the Balearic Islands by rabbits, he wrote, 'It is a well-known fact that the inhabitants of the Balearic Islands begged of the late Emperor Augustus the aid of a number of soldiers to prevent the too rapid increase of these animals. Ferrets are much prized on account of their hunting these animals; they are put into the burrows, with their numerous outlets, which the rabbits form, and from which circumstance they derive their name; and as the ferrets drive them out, they are taken above.' An important point in this passage is the suggestion that ferreting was a normal activity of soldiers for, if this were so, the probability that an army occupying Britain would bring both rabbits and ferrets would increase. Harting certainly had no doubt about it for he commenced his third chapter with, 'When the Romans introduced the rabbit into Italy they introduced the custom of hunting it with ferrets; and when they carried the same animal into Britain they imported the same custom with it.'

There is no lack of authors who support the theory of Roman introduction, and usually in categorical terms. What, for example, could be more positive than the jacket cover of Thomas's *Rabbit Shooting to Ferrets*, with its 'The rabbit has been hunted in this country with ferrets from the days of the Romans who learned the technique from the Greeks'? Or consider Whitaker in *Approach to Shooting*, 'Caesar's cohorts introduced the ferret to this country and with it its natural quarry, the rabbit, much in the same way as packs of foxhounds have been imported into Germany by regiments in occupation. In those days, although the pursuit of rabbits by ferrets was considered the sport of the "smart set", methods have probably changed little, for despite the theory that packs of ferrets were hunted by centurion field-masters, the historian Pliny mentions rabbits being "taken above", which seems to imply the use of nets.' Patrick Chalmers also writes of a Roman introduction and of 'smart centurions' hunting the rabbit with several couple of ferrets.

Now less critical people than you or I might be satisfied with all this evidence and feel the question adequately answered. In fact what do we know for sure? Neither Thomas, Whitaker nor Chalmers quote any authority for their statements and, without this, the presumption must be that their opinions—for, in the absence of facts, opinions they must be—were derived from Harting. Harting, in turn, appears to have no evidence of the Roman introduction of ferrets to this country for he is so painstaking and thorough that if he had he would have quoted it. All we know for sure is that the Romans used an animal which resembled a ferret in Italy and Spain—the rest is surmise. It may be that some scholar has come across evidence which would prove the point but, being a man concerned with some trivia such as major works of Roman art or sculpture and not appreciating the great importance of ferrets and rabbits, has passed it lightly by. In the absence of hard evidence our task is to apply logic to the facts we do have.

We are, you will recall, considering not only where the ferret came from but what it is, and if we cast doubt upon the Roman introduction we also raise a question over the 'wild weasels of Africa' origins. Harting himself, in spite of his advocacy of the Romans, has reservations, writing, 'Many writers have asserted that the ferret is a native of Africa, but the statement lacks confirmation from the fact that the animal has not been met with in a wild state in any part of that continent, where, however, other kinds of weasels exist.' He continues, 'The better opinion is that the ferret is merely a domesticated variety of the polecat, with which it is frequently crossed for the purpose of improving the breed.' Before considering the argument in depth let us look finally at what, to me, appears to be the nub of the Roman introduction theory. Lovable as ferrets may be, they are not, by themselves, likely to be kept as pets alone, and no one would introduce the ferret unless there were rabbits to be pursued. From this springs the almost irrefutable conclusion that whoever introduced the ferret also introduced the rabbit.

As we have seen several authors credit the introduction of the rabbit to the Romans, but you will recall that while the previous chapter contained arguments for both a Roman and a pre-Roman introduction, the most likely source remains the Normans. If this is true they also brought the ferret either at the same time or once the rabbit was well-established. However, the theory, to be examined shortly, that the ferret is simply a domesticated polecat, remains sound whether the introduction was made by Normans or Romans, for the polecat was, and is, widespread throughout Europe and could as easily have been domesticated by either of this country's conquerors.

However, all this said, you may prefer the safer but defeatist conclusions of Everitt, who wrote, 'By whom and when ferrets were first introduced into this country is not known, but certain it is that they have been used by our ancestors for the past five hundred years at least', or the Game Conservancy's Rabbit

Control booklet, 'The precise origins of the animal are lost in the mists of history.'

Having dealt mainly with where the ferret came from we now turn exclusively to what it is, giving, once again, priority to the views of the layman and then turning to the scientists. In fact the view that the ferret is a domesticated polecat is so prevalent that it is not so much a question of what it is but whether it is or is not simply a tame polecat. There is not, of course, any doubt about the ability of our forefathers to trap wild polecats. (Writing in the sixteenth century, Mascall, in *A Booke of Fishing, etc.* (1590), described a device called a hutch, used for catching polecats.) However, taming a wild adult polecat would be difficult, if not impossible, and the more likely technique would be to capture a young litter. Niblett, incidentally, states that wild polecats kept in captivity are very liable to go blind, but does not claim any personal experience of this.

There is no point in listing many examples where authors claim, or even take for granted, the derivation of the ferret from the polecat. A couple will suffice. In his classic *Wild Sports of the Highlands*, Charles St. John wrote, 'There is no difference in appearance between the polecat and the brown ferret, who also partakes very frequently of the shyness of his wild relative.' And Payne-Gallwey in *Letters to Young Shooters*, said that ferrets exactly resembled foumarts (a common name for the polecat), but were smaller. The question of the smallness of the ferret, when compared to the polecat, bothered me for some time, for the natural consequence of domestication of a creature is for it to grow larger, not smaller—there are countless examples from geese to rabbits to prove the point. Yet the average weights of polecats are, respectively, 2¾ lb. (1·25 kg) for the male and 1¾ lb. (0·8 kg) for the female—well in excess of the average weights of hob and jill ferrets. Samuel and Lloyd in *Rabbiting and Ferreting* express their surprise over this point but offer no explanation. Harting does, suggesting that their reduced size is due to the inferior conditions in which they are frequently kept. I find this explanation not entirely satisfactory and, were it not for the scientific material which follows, would be happier to believe that a ferret is a domesticated stoat grown larger rather than a domesticated polecat grown smaller.

One common belief among old-time writers and supported by no less an authority than Gilbert White was that there were two separate species of ferrets—the brown or polecat and the white. For example those two pillars of the sport, Walsingham and Payne-Gallwey, writing in *Shooting* (Badminton Library, 1889) said, 'For ourselves we have a preference for the white species over the brown or "polecat" kind. It is said that these latter are a cross between the ordinary ferret and the true British polecat, and probably this is the fact.' Everitt, who took his ferrets very seriously, went into detail in his book as to whether a cross-bred animal, that is the progeny of a polecat and ferret, or a pure-bred, was best. In practice there were probably very few genuine cross-breedings between a wild polecat and a ferret, principally because of the need firstly to catch the polecat which was already becoming scarce by the time the various authors we are considering had appeared. In view of the common ignorance about ferrets it is much more likely that when a countryman talked of a cross-bred ferret he meant a mating between two ferrets, one white and one brown. Everitt, in fact, makes particular reference to a doe ferret which escaped and mated with a polecat, mentioning the exceptional boldness, energy and courage of the young in such terms as to suggest the event was a rarity.

The truth, I am sure, is that ferrets are ferrets whatever their colour, and that white ferrets are merely albinos. Although albinos are rare in any species it is likely that many generations of ferret keepers would have bred from them for two good reasons. Firstly, albino or white ferrets are usually, but not invariably, less wild and consequently more manageable than 'polecat' ferrets. Secondly, their light colour is much more visible against a dark background, a feature rapidly appreciated when trying to spot a small creature in a ditch of dead leaves in poor light.

In passing, it is interesting to note that there were many old country names for the polecat; those that I have been able to trace being foumart, fitch, fitchet and fitchet-weasel. Foumart derives from foul-marten, a description owed to the odour normally associated with this family. A fitch was a sixteenth-century name for a brush made of polecat's hair, but whether the common name for the animal came from the brush or vice versa I cannot tell.

At this point we move from country guess-work into the factual world of the scientist and I must confess that much as I love the former I am always more impressed by the latter. I will start by quoting two major authorities. Van Den Brink, in *A Field Guide to the Mammals of Britain and Europe* (1967), in his description of the polecat says, 'The ferret is often an albino or semi-albino, domesticated form, the origin of which is not yet clear.' 'Often' is interesting. If the ferret is often a polecat, as defined, then it is sometimes not—if not, then what is it? Or does Van Den Brink mean that when it is not an albino or semi-albino, domesticated form, it is a naturally coloured, wild one. Hardly, I would think, for would it not then be simply a polecat?

Harrison Matthews in *British Mammals* (1952) is less ambiguous, for when speculating that the period of gestation of the polecat is about forty days he says, 'The latter figure is probably correct, for in the ferret, which is merely a domesticated polecat, the period is forty-one to forty-three days.'

Scientists deal in truth, not opinions, and such categorical statements would not be made without solid foundations. Let us look at them.

The polecat is one of the large family of animals comprising the carnivores, all of which have teeth adapted to tearing flesh, and including such widely differing members as polar bears and weasels. Although this family survives by the destruction of other creatures its members have some engaging habits, among them their willingness to play, not only as youngsters but as adults. Dogs, badgers and otters all provide good examples and anyone who has kept ferrets in good, spacious conditions knows how they enjoy a rough and tumble among themselves. Harrison Matthews attributes this partly to their superior brain-power when compared to other animals and partly to diet. The concentrated food of the carnivores permits them leisure, whereas the herbivorous animals have to eat such large quantities that little time is left for play.

While the playful tendencies of the ferret are interesting they prove nothing and we must move on to more positive ground. Families are divided into different genera and these into different species. In the case of the polecat the genus is Mustiled and the species *Putorius putorius* LINN. Van Den Brink gives the ferret a sub-species *Putorius putorius furo*, but Harrison Matthews feels there is no justification for this. Now different genera cannot breed through several progeny; for example, a horse and an ass can produce a mule but this cannot reproduce. But some closely related species within a genus can reproduce and this fact provides a vital clue to the origin of the ferret. There is an abundance of evidence to show that polecats and ferrets can reproduce and that their progeny can go on reproducing generation after generation and, convincingly, at any stage a polecat can be introduced to ferrets and vice versa. In these circumstances there can be no question but that the ferret derived from the polecat.

At one stage, as I mentioned earlier, I had wondered whether the origin was the stoat, for, based on my earlier argument that domesticated wild animals grow larger, this would seem a more likely source than the polecat. However, this is conclusively disproved by the fact that the stoat and ferret cannot reproduce, being of unrelated species. (The polecat is *Mustela putorius*, whereas the stoat is *Mustela erminea*.) Over the centuries the polecat and the ferret must have been cross-bred many times, either through men deliberately trapping polecats to introduce fresh, wild blood into their ferrets, or by escaped ferrets finding a polecat mate. Although the species may differ, family ties ensure that ferrets never fight stoats or weasels which they must encounter on many occasions below ground. They do not, however, appear to like each other's company and only last spring we bolted a particularly large stoat from a Hebridean burrow with a most docile ferret. In terms of size and weight the nearest relative to the polecat is the mink, but here again, while the genus is the same the species is different. Harrison Matthews makes the interesting comment, whilst dealing with various sub-species of polecats, that, 'Even the Asiatic polecat from which the ferret is sometimes claimed to take its descent, is probably no more than a geographical race of the typical species.'

The same writer deals with an interesting claim, originating, I believe, from a paper produced by the Zoological Society, that the ferret can be distinguished from the polecat by the character of the skull. The skull of a ferret, when viewed in plan form from above has a 'waist', or narrows in the postorbital area; or, in laymen's language, about a third of the distance along the skull from the neck. The same characteristic is seen with the polecat but, and this is the essence of the argument, the 'waist' is much less pronounced. If this contention were correct it might point to the ferret being rather less closely related but the counter-argument was advanced that the difference was due only to diet. Apparently many species of carnivores brought up in captivity show skull differences from their wild brethren, due to eating softer foods. As a result the jaw muscles are used less vigorously and do not mould the growing skull of the young animal in the same way.

In fact, since the theory was first advanced two discoveries have thrown a veil of confusion over it. Firstly, some ferrets have been found with skull 'waists' the same size as polecats. Secondly, work by H. Tetley in 1939 (some six years *before* the 'waist' theory), also published by the Zoological Society, dealt with a sub-species of polecat, once found in Sutherland but now believed extinct, which had a narrow skull 'waist' comparable with the ferret.

Interestingly, although Harrison Matthews devotes nearly a page to the subject of skulls he gives only one sentence to the fact that the carnassial teeth of a ferret are usually smaller than those of a polecat. The reason, he suggests, may be either genetic or dietary.

To sum up. For my part I am satisfied that the ferret is a domesticated polecat; domesticated from Continental animals, brought to this country and subsequently inter-bred with our native stock.

As with the rabbit the ferret appears in various historical references although guidance to the date of its arrival in this country is negative rather than positive, namely, there is no mention prior to the appearance of the Normans.

The earliest reference I can trace appears in *Animals and Man* (1952) by G. S. Cansdale, who states, without quoting his source, that before the cat was introduced to ancient Greece polecats were used in and around houses there to control mice, and that these were probably the forerunners of domestic ferrets. He then goes on to provide some partial evidence by saying the same custom was found in Rome as Petronius commented that if pet birds disappeared it was the habit to blame the polecats.

Patrick Chalmers in *The Shooting-Man's England* reports that ferrets were used by Genghis Khan, but I suspect his source was once again Harting, who goes into greater detail, quoting from Ranking's *Historical Researches on the Sports of the Mongols and Romans* (1826). In this it is stated that ferrets were used by Genghis Khan in his Imperial hunting circle at Termed in 1221. Ferrets were also listed among the animals used for hunting by the Emperor Frederick II of Germany in 1245.

The first reference I have been able to trace of the ferret in Britain is in Lockley's *The Private Life of the Rabbit*, who quotes an account preserved in the Public Records Office relating to three islands off the Pembrokeshire coast. It occurs in the Pipe Roll of Edward III, and reads: 'Carcases and skins of rabbits caught in the islands of Schahney, Schokolm and Middleholm, Michelmas 1325 to January 30, 1326, £13 12s. Expenses: Stipend of 3 ferreters, 12s 3d; salt for the aforesaid rabbit carcases, thread for the rabbit nets, boards, nail and cord used for the boat in the said islands, 5s 2d.'

Next comes a statute passed in 1390, in the time of Richard II, prohibiting anyone from keeping or even using either greyhounds or *fyrets* who had not land or tenements of the annual value of 40s. Everitt quotes Strutt on the subject of ancient group terms that include a skulk of foxes, a cete of badgers, a clowder of cats, and in particular, a fesynes of ferrets. Harting, however, disagrees, quoting the *Book of St. Albans* (1486) as using the term a 'besynesse of ferettes'. Subsequent writers have interpreted this as a business of ferrets, although I wonder if this is not an over-simplification. Harting reports mention of both the *fychew* and the *fyret* in 1481 in Caxton's printing of *Thy storye of Reynard the Foxe*, and in 1486 in the *Book of St. Albans*. Nothing further is reported until 1621 when the *Household Book of Lord William Howard of Naworth* has several entries indicating the use of nets and ferrets to take rabbits in Cumberland. In 1649 there was an agreement for a warren in Hampshire, on Goddens Down, Micheldever, which permitted the warrener to use 'hayes dogges ferrets nettes and other engines'.

From this point on ferrets are mentioned too frequently for the occasions to be worth recording, but it would be a pity to conclude this chapter without mentioning some of the more interesting references to them.

Fanciers of other domesticated creatures go to great lengths to define the ideal characteristics of their particular animal or bird, but ferrets are rarely accorded so much attention. The best I can do is two descriptions, one from Everitt, on the selection of a dog ferret for breeding, who advised, 'Its body should be slim, lengthy and muscular, its legs and feet sound and strong, its face sharp, fur clean, glossy and thick, and it should be quick in movement. A stumpy, large-headed, dull-looking animal should not be used for breeding purposes.' The other definition comes from Niblett who says the general characteristics of the mustelines proper are all much the same, 'They all possess the same low, elongated, lithe, muscular bodies; they are all predatory, blood-thirsty, determined of purpose, and relentless; they are all constitutionally hardy, prolific, foul of odour, yet withal of scrupulously clean habits.' On the subject of odour, Everitt claims, 'When riled it emits a nauseous odour', but this is not my experience.

Although not the most perceptive of writers on the ferret, Everitt's book has many excellent anecdotes. One concerns a Mr. Lane of Wednesfield who wrote to Everitt in 1895 on the subject of a ferret suckling young rats. It appears one of Lane's workmen had a white jill ferret with eight young about three weeks old. One night the owner put six young rats, of about the same size of the ferrets, into the hutch, expecting them to be killed and at least partly eaten. Instead the following morning rats and ferrets were running about together. Five of the rats were taken away, presumably because the ferret could not be expected to feed fourteen young, and the jill suckled and reared the sixth with her own young. When the young ferrets were weaned the now fully grown rat and the ferret lived and slept together for six months, until the rat escaped through an unfastened hutch door. During this time hundreds of people came to see this strange sight, but the rat remained wild and shy and would hide under the straw. The most remarkable aspect was that the ferret was taken out ratting continuously and if a strange rat was put into the hutch would kill it instantly.

With the casual acceptance of animal suffering common to his time Everitt wrote, 'It is an interesting sport to get a large scalding tub, with a piece of netting over the top, placing a full-grown buck rat and a ferret in it at the same time, and watch the fight. As a rule the rat will be the first to show the white feather by an attempt to avoid meeting its adversary. The moment it does this the ferret has it by the throat like a flash of lightning, and the end is reached.' But of all Everitt's tales my favourite is of the old retired farmer who spent most of his time ratting, whilst wearing a weather-beaten chimney-pot hat. His delight, so we are told, was to take his catch home alive in the hat and, on meeting friends, apologize for not removing it, explaining that he had a 'full cargo'. 'Oftentimes a considerable commotion would be going on inside that hat, but he only banged it with a stick and said, "They'll be quiet enough when they get home tonight", which was certainly true, for, unless he had a larger number than usual, their lives would not be worth a day's purchase.' (They were destined to feed the old man's ferrets.)

Whilst on the subject of rats, Niblett says polecats have been kept in captivity and worked against rats in the same manner as ferrets. He quotes no source and I rather doubt this, suspecting this as yet another case of uninformed countrymen (not, I hasten to add, Niblett) confusing polecat ferrets with polecats. Once freed into a hole I would have put the chance of again picking up a wild, recently captured polecat as extremely remote. On the subject of polecats it is pleasing to be able to record that this once near-extinct mammal is now showing a healthy increase in both numbers and range. Wales is the great stronghold and in the central areas it is now described as very common. This is only a relative term, but there is no reason to fear the disappearance of this most attractive creature.

Apart from the fact that it is one of the few books entirely devoted to ferrets, Everitt's *Ferrets* is remarkable for an exhaustive examination of all aspects of the law touching on them. The length (no less than thirty-two pages) and authority of the treatment are such that I would cheerfully wager that Mr. Everitt was a lawyer. Virtually none of it is of the slightest use nowadays, and I very much doubt whether it had much application when it was written at the turn of the century. It is, however, well worth detailing some of the more interesting points, if only as an illustration of the value men once placed upon ferrets. Under the heading 'The rights of the owner', Everitt stated the right of an owner to recover an escaped ferret, even to the extent of using reasonable violence against a person who had wrongfully obtained possession of it and refused to give it up. To substantiate this he cites *Blades* v. *Higgs* (1861), 30 L.J.C. P. 347 as, indeed, he quotes various other cases to illustrate other points. Whilst such knowledge and thoroughness reinforces my belief in his profession it carries less weight in this direction than the complete lack of humour he displays in arguing his next point—the ownership of the young from a jill ferret which has been mated by another man's buck without the consent of the owner of the latter. With due solemnity it is concluded that the young belong to the owner of the jill, even if the evil deed is done by fraud or stealth, although the owner of the buck might claim the value of the service or damages for interfering with his property.

After several pages of argument Everitt concludes that although at one time a man's life could have been at risk for stealing a ferret, nowadays, at common law, no one can be criminally prosecuted for stealing another's ferret. The pang of anxiety this brought to me was rapidly dispelled by mention of a statute of 1861 which gave protection to 'any bird, beast, or other animal ordinarily kept in a state of confinement', and carried a penalty of six months in prison or a £20 fine. Granted the protection this extended to the ferret was not wholly certain ('I know not whether a ferret would fall in the statute or not'—Mr. Justice Stephen, Dig. Co. Law 230), but it is reassuring. Under the same statute there were heavy penalties for killing or wounding a ferret unlawfully and Everitt examines in detail the circumstances in which you may safely shoot a stray ferret on your land.

Everitt concludes that the natural inclinations of ferrets being what they are, an owner is obliged to confine them carefully and if they escape and, for example, kill a neighbour's chickens, an owner is liable for full compensation. One interesting point is the liability upon the man who borrows or hires a ferret neither to lose nor injure it, for the hazardous existence of a working ferret makes either of these two disasters quite possible. Fortunately the law appears only to impose a duty of 'reasonable care'; a requirement which means what it says and does not excuse those who accidentally shoot the ferret or leave the lid of the box unfastened. Guilt also descends on the man who borrows a ferret to go rabbiting and then uses it for ratting. (And so it should—the scoundrel!)

It is, perhaps, fitting to end this chapter on this slightly mysterious creature by considering Everitt's final pages which move into an almost Alice-in-Wonderland situation. Can ferrets, he asks, be lawfully distrained for rent? Perhaps they can, he concludes, but more probably they cannot. Can or can't, I'd like to see the modern rent collector prepared to try!

CHAPTER THREE

The Natural History of the Rabbit

In this complex world one might be forgiven for hoping that the rabbit, our old childhood friend, would be a straightforward creature, presenting an author with no major problems of description. After all it appears to lead a simple, uncomplicated life, and a few thousand words should suffice to cover its natural history. But no—indeed no! In their essentially scientific and extremely good book *The Rabbit*, Thompson and Worden's bibliography lists no fewer than one hundred and thirty assorted books and learned papers, ranging as widely as 'The apophyseal line as an age indicator for the wild rabbit' and 'Syphilis as a disease of wild rabbits and hares'.

My task in the next two chapters is to select and present those aspects of our subjects' natural history which will interest readers. In this I am helped by the fact that the more you learn about rabbits the more interesting creatures they appear, and the more you discover similarities between the behaviour of rabbits and people. To quote Lockley, 'Humans are so rabbit.'

Rabbits and hares are both grouped under the order Lagomorpha. This order is divided into two families; the Leporidae consisting of one genus of hares and eight genera of rabbits, and the Ochotonidae, the pikas, with only one genus. The latter family is of no interest to us, being smaller, lacking any (external) tail and living no nearer to this country than Russia. Of the nine genera of the family Leporidae the eight which relate to rabbits are scattered throughout most of the world, the European rabbit being *Oryctolagus cuniculus* LINN 1758. This, in turn, is divided into six sub-species of which 'ours' is *Oryctolagus cuniculus cuniculus* LINN 1758, and is found throughout central Europe, north of the Mediterranean region, and west to Ireland, although artificial introductions have extended it to many other parts of the world. The other five sub-species range around the Mediterranean area, with Morocco having no less than three.

Less scientifically, countrymen have also found their own names and groupings for rabbits. Prior to the eighteenth century rabbits meant only the young, the adults being known as coneys. The addition of various corruptions of the word earth eventually led to an area with a high density of burrows being known as a coneygarth, conyger or conigrie. Various varieties of the rabbit were known as 'warreners', 'parkers', 'hedgehogs' and 'sweethearts', although there is no unanimity over the precise meanings. 'Warreners' clearly means those rabbits which dwelt in established warrens, that is a half-way condition between wild and tame. 'Parkers', according to Samuel and Lloyd, live in open country; a name no doubt deriving from the time when large country houses had a surrounding area of parkland provided, I imagine, with the dual purpose of giving an attractive prospect and shielding the residence from the disturbance of agricultural operations. Sheail, however, classes 'parkers' as exotic specimens only, white, black or sandy, which would have been artificially introduced into private land. A further difference exists over 'hedgehogs', with Samuel and Lloyd classing these as dwellers in thick wooded areas, while Sheail describes them as rabbits 'of no fixed abode'—travellers from place to place. Personally I do not think there is any such thing as a foot-loose rabbit; while there may be restricted local movement for various reasons, rabbits are essentially home makers. 'Sweethearts' were rabbits bred in captivity, although the name is more likely to be derived from the affection of children for the young rabbits than any observation of the breeding habits of the parents.

Like so many apparently simple things, the more closely you examine the rabbit the more complex it becomes. The pelt is a good example, being formed of not one but three coats. Adjoining the skin is dense, soft undercoat; through this protrudes the longer coarse hairs of the main outer coat, and beyond this protrude sparser but longer hairs to form a third, but much less important coat. The colouring is determined by these two outer coats, and in winter all three coats are denser. The principle is the same as with wildfowl feathering, where a thick, down-like feathering next to the skin provides warmth and an oily, outer layer provides waterproofing. Colouring has many local variations but the standard is known as the common-grey. The predominating colour is grey-brown, which extends over the upper parts, lightening underneath, but turning to reddish-brown at the back of the neck. The throat and underpart of the tail are white, but the upper tail is blackish, as are the tips of the ears.

The feet are 'shod' with thick hair, giving a good grip on all surfaces. As with the hare but to a lesser degree, the hindlegs are much longer and stronger than the forelegs.

The average weight of a wild rabbit is 3–4 lb. (1·3–1·8 kg), but weights tend to vary from area to area, depending on the available food supplies. Harting in *The Rabbit* gives several reports of rabbits in the 4–5 lb. (1·8–2·25 kg) range, and a few over 5 lb. (2·25 kg). However, any 'wild' rabbit over 5 lb. must suffer suspicion as to the purity of its background, for such weights probably stem from an escaped domestic rabbit. Harting reports one such example when a 6½ lb. (2·9 kg) rabbit was killed near Norwich in 1891. This minor marvel was duly reported in *The Field*, but a week later a former agent of the estate announced that some tame ones had been turned down ten years earlier to increase the size.

Although basically one of the less vocal creatures, rabbits will grunt, growl, squeak and scream. Growling is associated with the danger signal of back-foot stamping and grunting usually indicates pleasure. Squeaking and screaming are an indication of terror rather than pain, and are really the same sound but at different intensities. However, Lockley frequently heard screaming when the rabbits fought at night to establish dominance. As the purpose of fighting is not so much to kill as control, the losing rabbit could end the fight by retreating and it would be likely to do this before becoming terrified. It is, therefore, possible that screaming can also accompany anger and other intense emotions.

Although the rabbit has been studied so extensively the accumulated knowledge is surprisingly patchy. Some areas have been documented in minute detail while in others it is difficult to trace any serious research. Hearing is one such barren ground. The size of a rabbit's ears, the way in which it obviously uses them, and the results of any simple tests easily carried out, all confirm that a rabbit's hearing ability is excellent. It would, however, be interesting to know just how excellent. Is it superior to a hare's or an owl's? At what distance can it hear how much? And is it better at high notes or low notes?

On the question of sight we know that the basic structure of the eye in rabbits, humans and birds is the same, but the rabbit has an advantage over us. Our eyes are in the front of our heads and forward facing, giving restricted vision, whereas the more widely spaced eyes of the rabbit permit useful vision over more than 180 degrees. You would, however, be unwise to wish for a rabbit's vision for it is almost certainly colour blind, viewing the world in shades of black, white and grey.

In one of the most telling sentences in his *Private Life of the Rabbit*, Lockley writes, 'In about the time it takes the helpless human child to walk and utter a few simple words the rabbit has become a tough citizen of his own underworld.' This implied criticism of the human race is softened if one considers the different survival rates of the two species, but the chief interest to us is its implications in considering the rabbit's brain. In this area there is no simple path to the truth, for whilst there is a wealth of literature on anatomy there is little on the mind. What we do know is that a rabbit's brain is primitive, and the ability of a domestic rabbit to learn simple tricks is rather less than that of a cat. Uneducated countrymen often credited the rabbit and other animals with cunning, but wrongly so. The great distinction between men and other creatures, and the reason why we are the most successful, is our far greater ability to reason and to learn from experience. The actions of the rabbit are mainly dictated from instinct and reflex actions; probably not at all from reasoning and only marginally from experience. Lockley's 'tough citizens' were surviving not through intelligence and shrewdness, but because a primitive brain, served by superb sense organs, had learned what defensive actions to take in response to given alarms.

In determining the life span of the wild rabbit the critical factor is not how long it can live, but how long the dangerous and arduous conditions of its life permit it. Domestic rabbits live for about ten years but this would be a remarkable span in the wild. Nor is there much help available from the literature on the subject, probably because ascertaining the age is far more difficult than other characteristics, such as weight. Life span is determined not only by avoiding death from predators and man but also by the far more complex question of the status of the individual within his own society. Dominant rabbits enjoy the healthiest burrows and the choicest feeding. As they age and lose condition and strength, others take over the better things in life, and the downward path of the old is accelerated. The contrast with human society is vivid—we support the weak, inadequate and aged, whilst the rabbits elbow them to one side. Within a short time they succumb to their harsh environment. As a result, the rabbits which are left are tough and successful. Until comparatively recently the human race maintained its level of both physical and mental toughness in the same harsh way. Now we have an unprecedented proportion of our race whose life span is artificially extended by either medical or social measures (and frequently both). It is a humane policy and there is, of course, no alternative, but it will be interesting to see where it has led us in a few thousand years.

Lockley gives an excellent illustration of social pressures shortening the life of a rabbit in the case of 'Brown Boy'. This was a rabbit with an estimated age of 4 to 5 years, which had been dominant in his warren for a year but was deposed by a younger buck one autumn. The exact date was unknown but by the November he was 'now in poor condition, scarred from wounds about the neck and ears', and by early December he was 'very thin, his left ear had two-thirds cut off and missing'. It was unlikely that Brown Boy would have survived much longer and Lockley removed him to a separate pen. Here, protected from the attacks of the dominant buck, he recovered, was given a wife, and was still alive when the study finished two years later.

I question elsewhere the extent to which the results of Lockley's observation might have been slightly distorted by the confined circumstances of the subjects. Additionally, the inevitable presence of humans must have inhibited predators. For this latter reason his statistics on survival and age are likely to be rather better than would be found in a truly wild environment and vividly underline the harshness of nature. Eighteen months was found to be the average life-span in his enclosures, and by a little simple arithmetic he concluded this must also be the maximum average for truly wild rabbits, for they would otherwise over-populate the land. Interestingly, he makes the point that wild rabbits in captivity live for at least the ten years expected from a domestic rabbit. It follows that the very short life-span of a free wild rabbit is due to the dangers of its existence rather than any biological shortcomings.

The work of H. N. Southern (see Select Bibliography p. 212) demonstrates the very high mortality rate (and therefore the short life-span) of wild rabbits. In one breeding season the 36 does in a study warren produced 280 young, which lived long enough to emerge from underground and feed. Of these no less than 252 disappeared in the season, most of which were probably taken by predators. Additionally, 59 of the 70 adults disappeared; a more telling statistic, for these were adult animals, which had learnt the rules of survival.

It is very difficult to tell the age of a fully grown rabbit. The young and the, rare, very old are distinguishable but those in between defy easy assessment. As rabbits age so their ears become more leathery and tough, and their nails lengthen and become ragged. Beyond these features few books have any suggestions to offer, but those that do provide fascinating examples of how observant countrymen can arrive at the same conclusions, but without knowledge of the detailed reasons, as the scientists. Thomas, the highly practical rabbit shooter, was aware that bones could play a part in determining age and said the young can be separated from the old by pressing the backmost parts of the lower jaw together. In the young they are springy and break easily, whereas those of the old are hard and strong. Sedgwick confirms this in *The Young Shot*.

What Thomas observed is actually the basis of a much more scientific method of determining whether a rabbit is older or younger than forty-one weeks. In the study of any creature it is important to evaluate the contribution the young make to breeding in the year after birth, and this particularly so when determining the effectiveness of different methods of control of a pest species. In this case the problem is that rabbits reach adult size at four months and it then becomes very difficult to tell young from old.

The essence of this method is that even after an animal has reached full body size the epiphysis of its long bones have not fused with the shaft or diaphysis. (That is to say, those parts of the bones which are formed from a separate centre of bone-forming tissue have not yet fused, or joined, with the rest of the bone.) Nineteenth-century naturalists were aware that bone development continued after full size was attained and used this to distinguish between apparently otherwise adult rabbits. The details of subsequent research are given by Thompson and Worden in their chapter on physiology, and ageing is now carried out by reference to the epiphysial cartilage between the head and shaft of the tibia. Ageing cannot be carried out more accurately than to the nearest month, but, for practical purposes, rabbits with the apophysis still unfused can be regarded as not having reached nine and a half months.

It was after I had digested this, nodding gravely at the wisdom of the scientists, that I came across the following in Harting's *The Rabbit*, first published in 1898, 'One may tell an old rabbit from a young one by feeling the joints of the forelegs. When the extremities of the two bones which unite to form the joint are so close together that no space can be felt between them, the rabbit is an old one. On the other hand, if there is a perceptible separation at the joint the animal is a young one, and is more or less so as the bones are more or less separated.'

The contents of this chapter so far do not give any reason to expect the rabbit to be a great biological success and to be numbered with brown rats and wood pigeons in their ability to survive and multiply. It is, after all, almost incapable of defence and much preyed on by other creatures and man. The young, in particular, are both succulent and relatively easy prey. How do they survive so well? Part of the answer is sheer weight of numbers, and we come shortly to their great reproductive powers. Other less obvious factors favour them. They are tough—for example, we have previously considered the evidence from Mull of their ability to tolerate wetter conditions than sheep; they are also highly adaptable, living happily in a variety of environments; and most important, they are herbivorous. Although rabbits are highly selective grazers, they enjoy a wide range of alternative food sources and, unlike carnivores, very rarely starve. Finally, and most important, are the twin habits of living underground and being mainly nocturnal. Killing rabbits is a relatively simple matter—eliminating them, or even achieving a permanent reduction in numbers, is not. This is well illustrated by the records of the enormous numbers of rabbits trapped on various estates prior to myxomatosis, without having any lasting effect. It was a common belief among landowners that trappers, even when paid to clear an area completely, left a breeding population to ensure their future employment, but modern knowledge suggests they were, perhaps, unfairly maligned.

The versatility of rabbits extends to both swimming and climbing. Both Sedgwick and Harting report that they not only swim but swim well, and the latter, with his usual thoroughness, lists two actual incidents, together with the dates and names and addresses of witnesses. J. G. Millais in *British Deer* (1897) shows a sketch of a rabbit swimming which he is reputed to have made by catching live specimens, placing them in the water and having someone row him alongside while he drew.

Although swimming appears to be done only in an emergency, climbing is done by choice to an elevated 'form'. A favourite site is the bole of a pollarded tree, or the hollow interior of a decayed tree. I have seen cases of rabbits using the thatched roofs of derelict cottages in the Hebrides, reaching them via the partially collapsed stonework. A famous sportsman who reported the phenomenon of arboreal rabbits is Col. Peter Hawker in his *Instructions to Young Sportsmen* (1814).

Having considered the strengths of the rabbit it is now appropriate to consider its enemies other than man. Far more creatures eat rabbits than actually kill them—a roadside corpse can provide sustenance for such diverse feeders as crows, magpies, jays, rats, hedgehogs and beetles, but these are merely opportunists and our interest lies with the rabbit's true killers. In this context it is interesting that when many of the warrens were destroyed in the nineteenth century many naturalists felt that rabbits, now deprived of the artificial protection offered by man, would be exterminated. (See Thomas Bewick, *A Natural History of British Quadrupeds*, 1814.) Subsequent developments in rabbit ecology have contributed to the now common belief that it is not predator numbers which control prey numbers, but vice versa. We are still not fully conversant with the delicate balance in the various food chains, but a good food supply is a prime requisite for any predator population increase. A good example is the great decrease in the numbers of buzzards in Wales and the West Country which followed the arrival of myxomatosis.

In strict fact the natural interplay between rabbits and their predators has never been allowed a free hand. Throughout the centuries that the warren was a regular feature of the countryside the warreners destroyed predators ('vermin' in those days) as a regular duty. As far back as 1590 Leonard Mascall in *A Booke of Fishing* described the use of poletraps to catch eagles and kites and a form of hutch, baited with dead rabbit, for taking polecats. Before this human protection was withdrawn, with the destruction of the warrens, a new, albeit inadvertent, phase of man's intervention began. The new sport of shooting became popular and, once game rearing became common, the keeper arrived on the scene to continue the war on the rabbit's enemies.

Rabbits are least troubled by flying enemies so we will dispose of them first. The golden eagle will kill and fly off with an adult rabbit; but the eagle is a very small threat, partly because there are comparatively few of them, but also because, in those isolated areas where the eagle survives, the rabbits, in common with the hooded crow, are most numerous around the oases of human cultivation; places which the eagles avoid.

Lockley states that buzzards and harriers kill grown rabbits but cannot lift them without great difficulty. Harriers I cannot speak for, but I doubt buzzards kill adult rabbits. If they can kill a rabbit they can kill a grouse and I have never found a record of this happening. The truth, I believe, is that buzzards kill and take young rabbits and, indeed, Lockley appears to confirm this in his book. He describes how the buzzards would sit in the great elm on a fine afternoon, waiting for the rabbit kittens to appear, when they would glide down and take them in their talons. In this description he establishes the presence of rabbit-eating buzzards in his area. If they took the young in the summer, a time of plenty for predators, they would certainly take the adults in the lean times of winter—if they could. Sheail says, 'The buzzard also looks to the rabbit for prey,' and reports that Colonel Ryves in his book *Bird Life in Cornwall* (1948) called the buzzard the 'Great Rabbit Hawk'. None of this is evidence that a buzzard kills an adult rabbit, and I think the misconception comes from people seeing buzzards eating rabbit carrion. I have personally disturbed many buzzards from Hebridean road verges eating rabbits killed by passing vehicles. And Thompson and Worden, in their chapter on myxomatosis, report the bodies of diseased rabbits being attacked by buzzards.

Looked at logically it would seem essential that if a buzzard is to kill an adult rabbit it must do so almost instantly, for if it does not the rabbit will probably break free. In fact, I doubt a buzzard can kill a rabbit instantly, an opinion based on a dramatic sight I once viewed in Skye when, at a few yards, I watched a buzzard fall on a young leveret of about one half the size of a fully grown rabbit. It failed to kill it, but just, and only just, managed to rise with its prey and fly at a height of some 6 to 10 feet (1·8–3·0 m), with the leveret screaming in terror. (The mother hare appeared and ran underneath, leaping wildly, but that is another, and pathetic aspect.) If the buzzard could not achieve a clean, quick kill with a small leveret, its prospect of conquering a tough adult rabbit would be poor. What we really need to satisfy our curiosity is a study of the extent to which the length of a buzzard's talons permit them to enter the vital parts of a rabbit.

Having written these thoughts on buzzards, I passed on to owls but found my curiosity unsatisfied and decided to seek some expert opinions. I began by writing to the Hawk Trust and posed the simple question: Can a buzzard take an adult rabbit? The Secretary/Curator, Miss Caroline Hunt, kindly replied in detail saying that her buzzard had only taken two hedgehogs (!), but suggesting I write to Colin Tubbs of the Nature Conservancy Council and the author of the book *The Buzzard.* The essential part of his reply warrants quoting in full. 'I have certainly not seen a buzzard take an adult rabbit and almost all the prey material recovered from nests or pellets during my work on the buzzard has been of small animals. I would not, however, underrate the possibilities of a buzzard killing an adult rabbit even if the latter were running. Buzzards have surprisingly powerful talons and, moreover, can be remarkably agile. Given a little luck on the part of the bird, I see no reason why a buzzard should not achieve an instant kill, though, of course, it would be unable to lift the animal afterwards.'

The statement that almost all the prey material recovered was of small animals seemed an important indicator but, not being content, I wrote to Professor Davis, The Honorary Secretary of the British Falconers' Club. He replied, 'I must confess that most falconers would not consider a buzzard suitable for flying fully grown rabbits. They will, however, readily take half-grown ones quite well, although I have no personal experience of them doing so.'

So far the experts had, I felt, confirmed my view, but one paragraph in Professor Davis's letter threw doubt on the whole matter. He had, he wrote, just received an application to join the Club from a Mr. Peach of King's Lynn, who 'claims to have killed numerous rabbits with his buzzard'. This seemed so critical that I telephoned Mr. Peach and, immediately after, made a note of the conversation. Basically the facts were that he had trained two buzzards to attack rabbits by pulling carcasses through grass on the end of a length of string. Subsequently one of the buzzards had taken five adult rabbits and the other, two. Impressive facts, but the details were not so convincing. In all cases but one the rabbits had been stationary, and feeding, and the buzzards had sunk their talons into the back of the neck. In the one exception the grip had been into the head. In no case was the rabbit killed, but the buzzard held tight while the rabbit jumped about until Mr. Peach ran up and killed it. It was, he said, like 'a rodeo'. In a single case one of the buzzards took a slow moving myxie rabbit.

Mr. Peach's evidence, far from making me revise my theory that buzzards only take young rabbits, actually hardened it. There is no reason why these two tame buzzards should be either better or worse than wild buzzards at killing rabbits; nor is it likely that the unfortunate seven rabbits would have died quickly or even have been unsuccessful in eventually wrenching free. Neither is there any evidence in the fact that the buzzards actually attacked the rabbits, for they had been trained to do so. In my view a wild buzzard would not normally attack an adult rabbit unless conditions were such that it was ravenous.

Owls, including tawny owls, and all the members of the crow

family are charged with taking young rabbits and, although I have never personally witnessed an instance, I am sure they are guilty. The crow family, in particular, are so astute at picking up any meal on offer and young rabbits, when they first emerge into the world, are so innocent, that regular, sad encounters are inevitable.

One last unusual feathered threat is said to menace rabbits. Sheail writes that where sea birds and rabbits occupy the same coastal areas there is often competition for nesting places, and he quotes several sources as reporting that puffins have evicted rabbits from their burrows in order to nest therein.

However much the rabbit may be in danger from the air, greater danger patrols the ground. It is threatened by (in decreasing order of size) foxes, badgers, dogs, wild and domestic cats, polecats, rats, stoats and weasels.

The fox takes both adult rabbits above ground and the young by digging out the litters from their stops. In the pre-myxomatosis days, when rabbits were numerous, it was estimated that they formed about half the fox's diet, although no formal research was carried out. With the arrival of the disease there were fears that foxes, which have always regarded man as operating a form of vulpine soup kitchen on their behalf, would become even more of a threat to sheep, poultry and other domestic stock. In the event there were complaints from those areas where foxes were traditionally a problem, but these have died away and the likelihood is that they merely underlined normal losses rather than heralded an increase. An interesting point to emerge from a survey on the feeding habits of foxes is that they appear to take fewer rabbits on high ground than low, the explanation being that the arduous living conditions on high ground provides more carrion than on the gentler low. One interesting snippet from the past concerns foxes. *Maison Rustique* (1600), discussing the practice of warreners of keeping does and young in hutches to protect them from poachers and predators, recommended keepers not to keep the young so enclosed for too long as it gave them a 'slumbering disposition' and made them easy targets for foxes, etc.

The leisurely badgers' excursions against the rabbit begin and end with digging up the young from their stops. Few would deny them this occasional culinary pleasure.

As a matter of passing interest, if a rabbit corpse is found with part missing, including the skin, the culprit is a fox, and this is further confirmed if the remains are lightly buried. Country lore insists that if a rabbit skin is found intact as if removed by human hands, then the killer is a badger. This, I must confess, puzzles me, for short of trapping the mother in her stop I cannot see how any healthy adult rabbit can fall to a badger.

The threat from dogs will vary widely from area to area, depending upon the degree of local tolerance to roaming dogs. In those areas where game is preserved their careers are likely to be brief. In any event not many dogs possess either the speed or the cunning to catch more then the occasional adult rabbit, and losses through this cause are probably small.

Wild cats, on the other hand, are very efficient rabbit killers, but are now so rare that their effect is infinitesimal. Domestic cats are a different story, for although they are unlikely to have the weight and strength to hold and kill an adult they can deal very adequately with the young and, unlike wild cats, roaming domestic cats are very common. Every keeper's hand is against them, of course, but local politics prevents many an execution.

Polecats also come into the class of being highly efficient killers which are now very rare. A note from the Mammal Society showing the distribution in 1963–7 records that there is a considerable extension in the range of the polecat, but sightings numbered less than 200 in four years, with the great majority occurring in the remoter parts of Wales. The reputation of the polecat as a rabbit killer is illustrated by a contributor to the *Agricultural Gazette* of 1844, who wrote, 'Three or four dozen polecats, martens or young kittens could be introduced to an area and soon there would be no rabbits to be seen.'

A rat cannot kill an adult rabbit, and I can find no record of one even attempting the feat. However, rats are responsible for the death of many young rabbits, from birth in the stop until they achieve sufficient size and strength to be an impractical quarry.

With the exception of the fox the animals we have dealt with so far are not, taking an overall view, major predators of rabbits. No such criticism can be levelled against those two star performers—the stoat and the weasel. The ability, at least of the stoat, to kill rabbits of all ages is unquestioned, and Sheail quotes *A Game-*

keeper's Note-book by Owen Jones and Marcus Woodward (1910): 'No hunt is more determined, ferocious, or relentless than when a stoat hounds a big rabbit to its death.' It is a common belief among countrymen that stoats and weasels perform some form of dance which attracts the attention of the rabbit to the point of hypnosis, until, drawing ever nearer, the performer transforms into a killer. Whether this is true or not I cannot say. In the absence of detailed reports from reliable observers the presumption must be that these are old wives' tales, but so much of country lore is based on at least an element of truth that I am reluctant to be dogmatic. The more likely explanation is that the stoat or weasel wears down the rabbit by sheer tenacity. There are various accounts of individuals who have saved rabbits at the instant that the stoat or weasel was about to kill, and these frequently speak of the rabbit being in a state of hypnosis. This is probably auto-suggestion, arising from the 'dance of death' myth, whereas the truth is simply that the rabbit is in a state of advanced terror.

Harting, a most meticulous observer, recorded that he had several times watched a stoat kill. 'He will not only enter a burrow like a ferret and cause the inmates to bolt, but will pursue a rabbit into the open like a foxhound, and sooner or later overtake and kill him.'

However, it by no means follows that a meeting between a stoat and a rabbit inevitably ends in the death of the latter. Harting gives two instances, as usual supported by names, addresses and dates, of witnesses who saw doe rabbits attack and drive off a stoat and weasel respectively, which were attacking young rabbits. Other reports confirm that in defence of their young, rabbits, probably does, show great courage.

The great disparity in size between a rabbit and a weasel leads me, at first thought, to question whether a weasel really can catch and kill an adult rabbit. Lockley throws some doubt on to their ability by stating, 'Weasels are in fact seldom seen to kill strong mature individuals.' However, there is no shortage of first-hand and reliable observers. Two instances will suffice. Jefferies in *The Gamekeeper at Home* (1880) gives a long account of a chase which, whilst obviously fictitious in itself, is equally obviously based on observation. In this two interesting points emerge. First, a weasel will relentlessly pursue one particular rabbit to the exclusion of others it may encounter in the hunt. This is logical; for if, as Jefferies also confirms, it wears its quarry down by sheer persistence, it cannot afford to change to a fresh rabbit. Second, he claims that once a hunted rabbit leaves its own burrow it is unwelcome in strange burrows and is driven out by the inhabitants. At first thought this seems far-fetched, but I suggest you reserve judgement until we reach the matter of the social structure of a burrow.

Our other observer is Charles St. John, who wrote in *Wild Sports of the Highlands*, 'I have frequently seen a weasel, small as he is, kill a full-grown rabbit.' Interestingly, he continues, 'The latter is sometimes so frightened at the persevering ferocity of his little enemy, that it lies down and cries before the weasel has come up.'

Another favourite item of country lore is that stoats and weasels join together to hunt in packs. Here evidence appears very scanty. Nowhere can I find any authoritative statement on the extent to which young stoats or weasels accompany their parent or parents, but logically it is unlikely that the young move, at once, from complete dependence, with the mother bringing food to them, to complete independence, when they separate and catch their own. Young stoats are sexually mature, and therefore able to lead separate lives, at eight weeks. Young ferrets are quite mobile by four weeks and very much so by six. Combining these facts suggests that from about the age of four weeks, but only for a short time, families of stoats can be seen moving together, or as a 'pack'. The period of pregnancy of a weasel is not known but from mating to lactation is thought to be about ten weeks, and, once again, family parties can be expected.

Given this, it is not surprising if countrymen of the older school, who were inclined to seek the more dramatic explanations, assumed these parties to be hunting packs. To the close observer there might be a size difference between adult and young, but this would not be obvious with such fast moving animals in summer cover. (Stoats only have one litter a year, and this in April or May. Weasels have two between April and September.) In a sense they would be a hunting pack, but if my explanation is correct the true hunting would be done by the parent or parents and the remainder would be tagging along for the meal.

Most books on this subject are vague, but Charles St. John

says, 'Occasionally these animals join in a company of six or eight, and hunt down rabbit or hare, giving tongue and tracking their unfortunate victim like a pack of beagles.' Nothing here suggests personal observation, and the picture of a pack of stoats giving tongue whilst pursuing a hare stretches the imagination overmuch. Jefferies is more convincing. He says both weasels and stoats will work in couples (which, during the breeding season, is logical enough, and a different thing to packs), and also in greater numbers. He reports seeing five weasels working a sandy bank of rabbit holes, but, on this occasion, lacks accuracy, one moment saying that alarmed rabbits were darting in all directions and the next that the pack ran their quarry out of the bank and into a wood, where he lost sight of them. His description would exactly fit a weasel family running happy riot through a burrow. He says stoats also work in couples, but seldom in large numbers.

All in all, I will stick to my theory of family parties moving together for a brief period of time before the youngsters make their own way in the world.

Those aspects of the natural history of the rabbit which have been covered in this chapter are of general interest, but many of them have been known to naturalists and observant country dwellers for centuries. It is only in recent years that scientists have discovered that the social structure of the rabbits' world is far more complex than we realized, and this is the subject of the next chapter.

CHAPTER FOUR

The Natural History of the Rabbit continued— Its Social Structure

It is likely that no other book has done more to lead the average unknowing, and probably uninterested, member of the British public into a close and informed knowledge of the natural history of a wild creature than Richard Adams's *Watership Down.* In his foreword Adams acknowledges that the book was inspired by Lockley's *The Private Life of the Rabbit*, which is based on Lockley's personal observations over a five-year period of rabbits artificially confined, and so carefully watched that he even constructed underground quarters from which he and his collegaues could keep constant watch on the interior of the warrens. It is a remarkable piece of study and essential reading for everyone who wants to know more about the rabbit. Looked at from a purely scientific angle it is not immune to criticism on two counts. Firstly, the need for constant observation made it necessary to confine the rabbits and to view them at all times both above and below ground, and both these factors may have influenced behaviour. For example, young rabbits were unable to wander from the warren to new territories and predators were possibly partly kept at bay by the frequent presence of men. Secondly, the book was written for popular reading and, just occasionally, I wondered whether the desire to please a largely emotional readership had not slightly influenced the author's conclusions. These minor carpings apart, however, it remains a remarkable book, and a major step forward in our understanding of the rabbit.

In this context it is noticeable how so much of our improved knowledge of rabbits centres on their social behaviour. Harting's book published in 1898 is packed with those practical facts about the rabbit which one would expect to be gleaned by intelligent countrymen, but there is no mention of social behaviour. The great advance in this area was made by H. N. Southern, who studied a Berkshire warren over a three-year period by capturing some of the population, pinning numbered celluloid discs inside their ears and releasing them. His work taught us a great deal about feeding and sexual behaviour, aggressive tendencies (which two aspects are of course linked) and the role of the doe. Thompson and Worden drew deeply on Southern's work for their book, published in 1956, but, even with the addition of their own observations, our knowledge of the actual social structure of a warren was limited. It was known that 'the social organization of the warren during the breeding season is built up from the territorial conservation of the does and the dominance of certain of the bucks.' It was also observed that the young males were encouraged to leave the home warren and that of those that remained only the strongest survived among the older rabbits.

At the time of the publication of Thompson and Worden's *The Rabbit*, Lockley was in the middle of his period of study, and, in 1964 his book appeared to reveal the full extent of the almost human-like relationships that exist in a busy warren of rabbits.

It is obviously impossible for me to give more than a brief resumé of so complicated a subject and I do urge those who have not read both Lockley and Thompson and Worden to do so. Your opinion of the rabbit and the way it has adapted to survive will be much enhanced.

To use Lockley's description, the heart of each warren is the royal family, the most powerful, generally the oldest, buck and doe, surrounded by their children and grand-children, and possibly a leavening of visiting strangers from nearby warrens. Exactly as in a human society there are the privileged and the underprivileged—the children of the dominant doe, herself enjoying the best grazing and therefore being in better condition, suckle to a higher standard and live in a dryer, superior part of the warren. Growing bigger and stronger they, in turn, are able to gain both better mates and better quarters and thereby ensure the continuing dominance of their line. If the warren is crowded there is often no room for the children of inferior does and these will have to disperse to new territories. The bucks, which fight during the breeding season, have a period of armistice during July to October inclusive, when they may even share a burrow with their main enemy of a few weeks previously. Few of the young bucks of the year grow large and strong enough to secure a mate of their own until the following season and must either exist in a condition of dominance or disperse. It is from these dispersals that new warrens commence, beginning with a pair which will either open a new burrow or re-colonize an abandoned one. As in so many societies the work is done by the woman, with the pregnant doe doing the digging, while the male restricts his efforts to feeding, mating and driving off other males. The first litter of kittens is born in the early spring and by the end of the summer the original doe will have had from two to six litters. Given the absence of disease and other adverse factors, the new colony will be well-established. It too will go through the same processes of social organization as the original warren, with the strongest and most active taking the best quarters, feeding and mates, and the remainder fitting into the particular level their own strength permits. As a result the strongest will survive best and the weakest will be the first to die whenever adverse circumstances occur. Harsh and cruel—true—but very much to the advantage of the race generally.

This brief consideration of the function of a new colony is a convenient moment to look at where rabbits prefer to build, and how. Both burrow and warren are loosely used, nowadays, to to describe a collection of rabbit holes. Originally a warren was artificially created for cropping or harvesting rabbits, but now the term is usually applied to a large burrow, or several burrows in close proximity. Really large natural warrens are now almost non-existent, partly because agricultural practices usually destroy them, but also because they are easily gassed. The largest warren of my acquaintance is on the National Trust property of East Head in Chichester Harbour. This is a peninsula of sand which is left in its natural state and where gassing is impossible due to the porous nature of the soil.

By choice the rabbit seeks well-drained, sandy soil, in which digging is an easy task and the finished quarters are dry. It avoids low ground, liable to flood and with dense vegetation, and very high ground because of cold and inferior grazing. Its preference is for open countryside with areas of woodland offering good, dry ground cover. However, these are preferences, not essentials, and they dig through loam, chalk, clay, and even coal seams. As recorded earlier most burrow digging is done by the does and this activity is triggered off by pregnancy in the spring. Some autumn digging also takes place, when rain softens the ground, presumably when the increased population from the breeding season has made conditions crowded.

The usual digging technique is to back out with a load, but Lockley records cases of does pushing the earth out with their chests. It is assumed that sloping sites are favoured as being dryer, but a subsidiary advantage is the way in which excavated soil falls easily from the hole entrance. A normal rabbit hole has a diameter of about six inches (15·2 cm) unless enlarged to form a chamber. Burrows are not constructed to any plan and if a rabbit meets a stone or other obstruction it either detours round it or stops digging. The result is the twisting confusion so familiar to ferreters. Burrows can be as deep as nine to ten feet (274–305 cm), but two to three feet (60–91 cm) is more normal. My own experience is that the easier working the soil the deeper the rabbits are inclined to dig. The size depends on the population, but increases are not always due to construction work from within. Whilst some does have their young in the main burrow, others will dig breeding stops around the periphery. Some of the young may continue to live in these, extend them, and eventually connect up with the main burrow. Lockley records the interesting fact that whenever rabbits in his colonies encountered wet ground they ceased digging in that direction.

Having digressed briefly on how and where rabbits construct their homes, we can turn to their behaviour within them. Although fighting and displays of dominance play an important part, once the social order is established the inhabitants live as a large family, observing territorial limits, but behaving to a pattern that assists overall survival. (Cynically, but with a measure of truth, one thinks of human life in a large, multi-storey block of flats.) Although rabbits are gregarious, Lockley observed they usually kept a few feet apart, as if by mutual consent, to establish a safety distance where no rabbit could take another by surprise. This is understandable in a world where force dominates, and where each leading or 'king' buck rules his particular territory so ruthlessly that he will fight to the death with any competing buck. Territorial limits are not vague but precise, and the buck marks them by scent, laying a colourless fluid from the glands under the jaw. True to human behaviour, while the bucks display the characteristics of possessiveness and aggressiveness the does like their home quarters and show no desire to do other than live peacefully in them. But, again, those bucks which fail, either in the younger, vigorous phase of their lives or in their old age, to maintain their territory are displaced and quickly die.

Life in an undisturbed warren in summertime must be far from unpleasant, with the does busily concerned with rearing and the bucks lazing around, keeping half an eye on their territory. Rabbits are by nature clean creatures, preening every part of the fur of their body with tongue and forepaws, in the same manner as a cat. In the same spirit they have no underground latrines, but establish special patches above ground, near to the warren or burrow, and usually on a small elevation, such as an old molehill. Lockley found that the rabbits' activities underground were almost nil, so much so that the observers found the utter boredom of watching snoozing rabbits made it difficult for them to remain awake. The indoor periods were, of course, during the day, for rabbits graze for most of the night. (In passing, there are various reports that rabbits frightened by ferreting or trapping will stay below ground for as long as ten days.) Normally they only emerge at dusk, but sunny afternoons bring them out earlier to bask in its warmth. Wind does not trouble rabbits, but rain does; a fact that will emerge in the ferreting chapter.

The question of whether rabbits pair faithfully or lead a promiscuous existence remains largely unanswered. Southern never observed copulation above ground, and having no form of night lighting—nor means of viewing life underground (as Lockley had) could not be sure which eventually mated with which. However, he made many detailed observations of sexual behaviour above ground, which he divided into five characteristic manifestations. These were: courtship chasing, where the buck would chase the doe above ground, sometimes furiously but more often casually, with both animals stopping regularly and looking at one another; tail 'flagging', mainly performed by the buck, when he would lay his tail along his back to display his white underside or scut to the doe; enurination, a somewhat remarkable method of displaying affection, where the buck emits a jet of urine at the doe; copulatory behaviour, where the buck would commence the preliminaries of copulation, only to be rebuffed by the doe; and finally, 'amatory' behaviour. This is merely displays of affection between a pair, such as licking and nuzzling.

An important point about Southern's observations is that although individual rabbits were marked he does not suggest any permanent pairing in their outdoor activities. Lockley, however, is quite definite that permanent partnerships are formed, and goes into great detail over the relationships between individual buck and doe pairs. Sadly, doubt is cast on these idyllic relationships a few pages later, when he considers the surplus of does to bucks in the community and reaches the conclusion that adultery must occur. Others have no doubt. Consider Simpson, in the last century, 'Nor in well-stocked warrens is the rabbit monogamous, for we find that the does produce freely when the bucks are much fewer in number than the does.' Although a few observations of actual mating have been seen at dusk the normal time must be night, probably after the more important business of grazing has been concluded, for Southern is satisfied that it rarely occurs above ground in daylight and Lockley, that none occurs underground. As a mere observer I derive a certain mischievous satisfaction from the rabbits' success in hiding their most intimate moments from prying human eyes.

Turning from sex to the more mundane matter of feeding should reveal a straightforward aspect of rabbit life. It does not, for we encounter, eventually, the remarkable activity of reingestion.

It is estimated that ten rabbits with a total weight of 40 lb. (18·2 kg) will eat as much as one sheep, weighing about 120 lb. (54 kg). In other words sheep are about three times more efficient convertors of grazing into meat. Granted the sheep requires much effort and expense to raise to full growth, whereas the rabbits manage very well on their own; but when the time for slaughter arrives the sheep is, as it were, to hand, while taking possession of the rabbit is so labour consuming that the value of the meat is often less than the labour cost. Lockley estimated that each of his rabbits required 150 square yards (125 m^2) of grazing, that is, approximately 35 rabbits per acre (0·4 h). This is a high density, brought about by his artificial confinement, but it supports observations of densities on small islands of 10 to 50 adults per acre. Such high densities usually create a population cycle in which numbers build up to a peak until over-crowding and malnutrition cause a spectacular crash, when the survivors, now living in spacious quarters and on abundant food, rapidly rebuild the population to their own, ultimate disadvantage. (Is there not a moral in this!)

In times of need rabbits will eat almost anything but, given a choice, they have strong likes and dislikes. Their greatest preference is for young plants and the damage they do in plantations, eating the shoots of seedlings and the bark of saplings, results in heavy expenditure by the Forestry Commission and others to fence them out. (William Gilpin, in 1804, complained that the rabbit nipped in the bud the growth of oak trees badly needed by the navy for ship-building in the eighteenth century.) Sheail holds the view that rabbits played a major part in destroying large areas of woodlands by preventing the growth of seedling trees which would otherwise have replaced trees dying of old age or felled for fuel. Certainly rabbits had, before myxomatosis, a major effect on the ecology and Sheail gives many informative details. For example, he reports Richard Fenton in 1903 explaining that the cheese made on Ramsey Island was better than that from other islands along the Welsh coast. Ramsey had few rabbits, and consequently clover and thyme flourished, to the betterment of the milk.

The full extent of rabbits on the countryside did not become apparent until myxomatosis virtually eliminated them. It then became clear that they had prevented the growth of physically dominant plants by grazing all vegetation cover and maintaining a low even cover overall. In many areas grass heath habitat depended entirely on the rabbit and with its disappearance other, larger growth began to engulf the open grassland. If one could, which one cannot, ignore crop and other damage, the rabbit would on balance be beneficial to the countryside. This is a personal view, biased by the pleasure the rabbit gives me as a sportsman, but there are strong ecological arguments to support it. I can certainly call on Harting, who wrote, 'Rabbits are unquestionably the kind of stock to make the finest turf: they bite closer than any other animal that grazes, and the best turf for gardens is that taken from warrens, or from downs upon which rabbits abound.' Harrison Matthews in *British Mammals* takes a less charitable and more scientific view, saying that rabbits not only graze herbage which should be eaten by stock but change the character of the vegetation. By close grazing the lateral buds of the plants are destroyed, normal regeneration cannot occur, and the valuable pasture grasses and clovers are extirpated and replaced by species useless to the farmer. Which theory would seem to fit nicely with the story of the flavour of the cheese from Ramsey.

Attempting to compile a list of the rabbit's likes and dislikes is not easy, as most authorities credit them with the ability to eat almost anything (e.g. Harting—'They will eat almost anything that is green') and then proceed to give a long list of their dislikes. Harting goes into the greatest detail, devoting several pages to listing plants and shrubs which rabbits avoid unless starving, and including a list prepared by Sir Herbert Maxwell in 1897 which 'may be relied upon to defy the attacks of rabbits.' This includes azalea, rhododendron, honeysuckle, hawthorn and dogwood. (Interestingly, among the likes he lists acorns, which, he says, rabbits eat with enthusiasm.) Sheail on the other hand believes rabbits are fastidious and says they tend to avoid many forms of plants. Lockley confirms their dislike of rhododendrons, and adds that even when very hungry they would not touch arum, lords and ladies, cowslip, primrose, burdock, comfrey and sorrel. He confirms Sheail's statement that rabbits destroy some plant species. With each summer the untouched burdock, comfrey and nettle invaded more and more of the pasture.

Nettles are, in fact, sometimes eaten, but only under great pressure. Thompson and Worden give a more up-to-date list of rabbits' dislikes, based on Tansley, and make the point that while rabbits avoid the less poisonous ragwort, they eat with impunity the poisonous foxglove and deadly nightshade.

On the subject of when they feed, Thompson and Worden say, 'Rabbits feed principally at dawn and dusk; although they may be seen grazing throughout the day in undisturbed places, and certainly feed at night.' Lockley partly disagrees in that while he says they graze in the early morning and late afternoon, he also makes the categorical statement, 'The rabbits remained grazing out of doors all night.' Did they graze all night or were they partly outdoors because it was pleasant to be there? Would rabbits, unpersecuted by man or predators, gradually resort to surface living because they prefer it? But we move into the realm of such unanswerable questions as whether duck feed at night because of centuries of persecution. Richard Jefferies gives us little help on feeding, for he credits rabbits with regular feeding times: 'In the very early morning, next about eleven o'clock, again at three or four, and again at six or seven.' He makes no mention of night feeding, which is a strange omission for such an accomplished naturalist, who also knew about the success of long-netting at night.

Personally, I have observed rabbits feeding during the daytime on many occasions, and obviously they do this where they feel safe. Rather unfairly one might observe that if Jefferies liked his three meals a day, at regular times, then the hours at which he believed rabbits fed were those at which he would be free to watch them.

Rabbits feed rather like a man scythes, rotating the head in a semi-circular movement until they have trimmed all reachable herbage, and then moving forward slightly. The rabbit being a gnawing mammal, its incisor teeth play an important part. The enamel coating is harder than the dentine, which forms the bulk of the tooth, and extends round the sides to the back. However, the enamel is thicker at the front than the back and as the dentine wears away the projecting enamel forms a sharp cutting edge. The incisors are constantly growing to compensate for the wear, and, if one incisor breaks off, its opposing mate will carry on unchecked, sometimes to the point where the rabbit cannot feed and dies of starvation.

Reingestion, put simply, is the rabbit's version of chewing the cud. When food is first taken it is formed into small, soft pellets, each contained in a membrane. These are evacuated in the usual way several hours after feeding, but are not allowed to fall to the ground. Instead the rabbit, by bending its head between its legs, takes and swallows each pellet individually, without breaking the envelope. The pellets return to the stomach, remaining intact for up to six hours before breaking down. At this stage the soft pellets contain about 56 per cent bacteria, of which the protein content is 36 per cent, and that of the plant matter 11 per cent. When this membrane envelope and other material have yielded their contribution to digestion and nutrition the waste forms larger, harder pellets which are then evacuated normally. Lockley's observations suggested rabbits were able to produce only soft pellets to be re-swallowed below ground and hard pellets above. Whether they are capable of determining which form of pellet is evacuated seems doubtful. More probably the process of reingestion takes place during the daytime, when rabbits are mainly underground and therefore away from a food source, and by evening the system is full of hard pellets awaiting to be evacuated.

Lockley suggests the process may have a partially defensive purpose, enabling the rabbit to eat rapidly and then take cover while it reingests at leisure. However, neither Thompson and Worden nor Harrison Matthews subscribe to this and regard reingestion as a purely chemical function to permit the better use of food.

One of the most interesting aspects is the time it has taken modern naturalists and scientists to rediscover that which was already known. The Bible (Leviticus 11) refers to hares chewing the cud; a Captain Cartwright in a book published in 1792 stated that rabbits ate their own dung; and in 1882 Morot published in a French veterinary journal results of experiments and an explanation of reingestion.

Apart from a few references Morot's work appears to have been completely overlooked until 1939, when Madsen of Copenhagen repeated and confirmed it, but even then considerable scepticism existed among scientists. This is well illustrated in Thompson and Worden who, quite unexpectedly, drop their strictly scientific approach to include a poem written by Dr. Tom Hare on the conclusions of Dr. E. L. Taylor who had been checking Madsen's findings. (Dr. Taylor was working for the Ministry of Agriculture and Fisheries at their Weybridge Laboratories and was, therefore, a civil servant.)

E. L. T. is very funny
    in stating that a normal bunny

Enjoying health and merriment
    Always eats its excrement.
To claim this for the Weybridge rabbits
    Does not surprise us, since their habits
Must conform with expectations
    and Civil Service Regulations.

Before finally leaving the rabbit's stomach and all the wonderful goings-on therein, I must touch on its drinking habits, or more correctly, its lack of them. In none of the authorities I have consulted can I find any mention of rabbits drinking, except for two negative opinions, viz. Lockley, who states categorically that they do not, and Simpson in *The Wild Rabbit*, just before the turn of the century, who said, 'I do not think that the rabbit ever drinks (laps) water in this country.'

We turn now to reproduction and, still being in a poetical mood:

The rabbit has a charming face
Its private life is a disgrace
I really dare not name to you
The awful things that rabbits do.

Anon.

Which is rather unfair to rabbits as their sex life is no more reprehensible than that of most other species, including humans—it is the impressive results rather than their actions which are responsible for their reputation. Rabbits are prolific breeders—they have to be, for being virtually defenceless and a food source for so many other species, it is one of their ways of surviving. (It has been a common sport of naturalists, over the years, to calculate the reproductive powers of rabbits, if left undisturbed. Bewick thought that one pair would in four years produce 1,274,840. Copland, in the nineteenth century, did the calculation differently and arrived at a four-year total of 2,164,800.)

Although rabbits will breed throughout the year, the main breeding season is from January to June, and during the peak of this period at least 90 per cent of adult does are pregnant. The female mates again about 12 hours after giving birth and, as gestation lasts some 28 to 30 days, she will produce about a litter a month. Fertilization occurs with almost unfailing regularity, for the eggs are not released from the ovary at regular intervals to take their chance, but are shed in response to the act of mating.

The usual litter size is 5 or 6 and females born early in the year, that is the strongest and healthiest, are capable of breeding before they reach adult size in about eight weeks.

This remarkable capacity to multiply is countered by a biological feature unknown to any other mammal except the hare. For reasons not yet clear, at least 60 per cent of all litters conceived are neither born nor aborted; the embryos die and are broken down within the uterus of the mother, the material forming them being taken back into her own body. Even in litters that survive to birth there is still an average loss, to reabsorption, of between 9 and 10 per cent. This amazingly high loss occurs on or about the twelfth day, and reabsorption of a complete litter takes place within only two days, leaving the female free to mate again.

Neither Thompson and Worden nor Harrison Matthews could suggest a reason for reabsorption, but Lockley felt confident that the stress of overcrowding was a major factor, and drew on the work of Myers and Poole in Australia to confirm this. His theory certainly makes most excellent commonsense, and we have only to draw on human experience to show that the miscarriage rate is higher among women suffering from stress and nervous tension in any form. If nature, as explained earlier, has arranged matters so that a mating almost invariably results in pregnancy, then some form of natural birth control is necessary to prevent rabbits from multiplying to the point where the population exceeds the food supply and starvation follows. Reabsorption provides yet another example of the practical countryman observing but not explaining a phenomenon before its discovery by the scientists. In *The Wild Rabbit*, Simpson writes, 'I have met with keepers who believed that in enclosed warrens rabbits were less prolific than they are in the open woods and fields, where they can scatter about more.'

Going back to the beginning, as it were, it is rare to see rabbits actually mate and detailed accounts are few. However, the act of copulation appears to be completed quickly, usually in less than fifteen seconds, with the female remaining passive, and with her body flattened to the ground. Ignoring, for reasons of space, the fascinating story of the travels of the resulting spermatozoa and all that ensues therefrom—which tale takes up eight pages in Thompson and Worden—there follows a pregnancy, assuming no reabsorption occurs, of some 28 to 30 days. Towards the end of this time the doe will make a nest, either in a short tunnel in the main burrow or warren, or more usually by digging a stop, and lining it with vegetation and fur plucked from her breast. At first thought it is strange that the doe should choose to have her young away from the shelter and company of her companions, but the buck has a tendency to destroy his young and the female hides them from him. Unlike the offspring of the hare, those of the rabbit are helpless at birth, lacking hair, sight and hearing. The doe hides the entrance to the stop with whatever material is convenient and then unlike human mothers, who at this stage swear this is the last, goes off to find her buck and start again. (Whether, in fact, she seeks a specific buck, or just a buck will depend, in my view, on the balance of the sexes in her burrow. However, men must be charitable to women in these matters so I write 'her'.) At this stage the young are known as a litter or kindle, and the individuals as kittens. Thompson and Worden say that little is known of the young wild rabbits' development in the nest, except that they emerge at about three weeks of age with an average weight of approximately 150 g. Sheail appears to be better informed, stating that 'They are blind until the eleventh day, their ears open on the twelfth day and they stand erect on the thirteenth day.' It would be interesting to know where he obtained his information. If from domestic rabbits it should be treated with reserve, for several research workers have noted that wild rabbits by no means follow the patterns of domestic in every respect. Certainly Lockley disagrees, stating that the hearing is completely developed at about the eighth day and the eyes open before the tenth day.

Whatever the truth the little creatures appear to be suckled only once each twenty-four hours; in spite of which they double their weight in the first seven days. Between three to four weeks they commence grazing outside the burrow, usually under the eye of the doe, with her next litter fast approaching birth, who summons them below if danger threatens by the conventional foot stamping and displaying her white scut. During the second month the young gradually become independent, but the extent to which they retain a relationship with their parents, or mother only, is not clear. Lockley is the only author I discovered willing to be positive and I found him somewhat contradictory. For example

(p. 113), 'Buck and doe accepted their progeny in the home for long after weaning time, and all through the neutral season—July to October—the growing youngsters might sleep by day in contact with the adults.' But later, (p. 151), 'But there is often no room in the palace burrows for the youngsters born to subordinate does in nursery stops outside the centre warren. While their natural gregariousness tends to draw them towards the bustling centre warren, it will depend on the degree of density there whether or not they are able to find an empty niche, a burrow or bolt hole unoccupied by the royal family and the royal entourage of "familiars"—relatives, children and perhaps grandchildren of the King buck and his queen.' In other words he says the young of the dominant rabbits are allowed to live in the warren, whereas the young of the weaker are driven out. I doubt it is as neat and orderly as this. If a rather strong and vigorous son of a 'subordinate' rabbit meets an unusually weak son of the 'Queen', I have no doubt he sees him off with the same rapidity with which the 'King' attends to the sexual desires of a 'subordinate' doe if the 'Queen' is not around.

Commonsense suggests events will be shaped by density. With an already overcrowded warren, few if any of the youngsters will find a home therein. Those that do will be the strongest. With a warren whose population is for any reason less than its capacity, the youngsters will make up the numbers.

The actual number of young produced by an adult female in one year varies with the quality of grazing available, assuming all other things being equal. Watson, working in New Zealand, estimated that dominant females could average five young per litter and have five litters a year, but the average was usually nearer twenty than this theoretical twenty-five young per season. Simpson, writing of warrens, thought twenty quite possible, but ten nearer the practical truth. Taking this country as a whole the average is believed to be between nine and ten and a half.

The common belief that wild creatures are healthy no doubt derives from the fact that it is rare to see a sick one. This is not, however, because illness is rare but because any serious disability is usually fatal, if not from the disease itself then from increased vulnerability to predators. If any proof is required a comparison of the life-spans of wild and domestic rabbits will provide it. In considering the diseases of the rabbit myxomatosis is of such importance that it warrants a chapter on its own later. It has, of course, been the subject of considerable research, but no really systematic survey of diseases has been done among British wild rabbits. Much is known about the diseases of domestic rabbits, and it is likely that these also occur in the wild. A formidable list includes a group of respiratory diseases; paratyphoid; pseudo-tuberculosis; a spreading necrosis of the lower lip; 'strangles' (caused by an abscess of the lower jaw); entero-toxaemia; rabbit syphilis; encephalo-myelitis; and so on through a variety of evil sounding conditions.

Those readers who, like me, have struggled to pull their pheasant poults through an attack of coccidiosis will be saddened to hear that it is also a major cause of death in rabbits. Other parasites of wild rabbits include liver-fluke, roundworms and tapeworms. Thompson and Worden have a very interesting and informative chapter which covers diseases and parasites fully, even to the extent of the fauna of rabbit carcasses.

CHAPTER FIVE

Myxomatosis—The Dreadful Plague

'What is certain is that we shall always have him [the rabbit,] not only in a sufficiency but in superabundance.' When Harting wrote this in *The Rabbit* in 1898 the future of the rabbit seemed secure. One could no more envisage a countryside without rabbits than rooks not nesting in elm trees or ploughs not drawn by horses. But no tragedy has ever struck the human race, neither disease, war nor natural disaster, with anything approaching the horrifying impact of myxomatosis upon the rabbit. Perhaps humanity's greatest catastrophe was the Black Death, the scourge of the first half of the fourteenth century. This plague entered Europe through the Crimea and in twenty years destroyed more than one-third of its population. Just to contemplate this disaster is frightening. Consider, then, that in many areas myxomatosis left only one rabbit alive in two hundred! In a matter of months a mammal which had played a major part in the ecology of the countryside for centuries was almost eliminated. It is hard to think of any other natural event so swift, ruthless and all-embracing, and also, one which divided country dwellers so sharply. Some, principally farmers, were pleased at this solution to the rabbit problem and actively encouraged its spread. Others, the majority, were aghast at the slaughter and the repulsive fashion in which the poor beasts died. (I found the disease so unpleasant that I have never eaten rabbit since; an illogical attitude, but one shared by many others.)

In the next few pages I will trace the history of myxomatosis, from its discovery at the end of the last century to its arrival and development in Britain. In so doing, I have leaned heavily on the writing of Thompson and Worden, for, whilst several books cover this subject, theirs is the most informative.

Although a relatively new disease to us, myxomatosis was first reported in 1898 in Montevideo, Uruguay, by Sanarelli, who attributed it to a filterable virus and named it 'infectious myxomatosis'. Some twenty years later, in Brazil, Aragão discovered the virus could be transmitted between rabbits by the cat-flea and subsequently he and other researchers found that mosquitoes could also act as vectors. In 1942 Aragão found that many of the native wild rabbits of Brazil had acquired immunity through a previous infection and those which were not immune only suffered a mild form of myxomatosis which was not fatal. This fact is of critical importance in assessing the rabbit's future in this country, for it shows that in time the disease will lose its virulence and have little effect on numbers.

The outward signs of myxomatosis are most unpleasant. After an incubation period of five to seven days there is a clear watery discharge from the eyes. Within a day or two the discharge thickens and the eyelids swell until, pressing tightly together and sealed by the discharge, the animal is blind. The bases of the ears and other parts of the body, particularly around the nose and chin, and the anus and genitals, may also swell. These swellings consist of a jelly-like tissue and, except for the few rabbits that survive, death comes between eleven and eighteen days after infection. Although infected rabbits appear to be at least partially deaf, my own view is that it is the general onset of death that renders them so slow to react rather than deafness. Even if prodded a badly infected rabbit will often hop only a few feet. Whilst at first sight the disease appears a dreadful affliction, experienced observers have told me that they do not think that it is very painful. They make the point that the immediate reaction of both animals and humans in pain is to go off their food. 'Mixie' rabbits do not, but continue to graze and bask in the sun to the end. Lockley even suggests that they will attempt to mate when only a few hours from death.

As the rabbit was more damaging to Australian agriculture than to any other farming community in the world, it was natural that the greatest efforts to achieve its downfall should be centred there.

Aragão's success in transmitting myxomatosis had seemed promising, and the New South Wales department of Agriculture obtained some virus from him. Laboratory studies were carried out, but the problem of successful transmission under field conditions seemed too great and the experiment lapsed. Years later, Sir Charles Martin, working in Cambridge, England, carried out successful trials and published the results in 1936. Sir Charles used two strains of myxoma virus, obtained from South America, and tested these on both tame and wild rabbits. The weaker strain killed all but 3 of 52 tame rabbits and the more virulent wiped out two colonies of 44 and 55 wild rabbits.

Although, surprisingly, Thompson and Worden make no mention of it, Lockley records how Sir Charles approached him in 1936 for permission to carry out a field test on Skokholm Island, Pembrokeshire, on which Lockley then lived. With some 10,000 rabbits on 240 acres (*c.* 97 h) and no external interference, it was an ideal spot for experiment, and Lockley agreed. That autumn 83 rabbits were caught, marked, innoculated with the virus and released. Twelve were found dead shortly after, but by the spring there was no trace of myxomatosis. Two further attempts were made to introduce the disease, but to the disappointment of both men, they failed, for reasons which will appear as this chapter progresses.

Encouraged by Sir Charles's 1936 results further trials were conducted in Australia, but with poor results. Partly because of the understandably cautious attitude of the health authorities the major trials were restricted to the thinly populated semi-arid pastoral areas of South Australia. This location, unknown to the scientists, had an important bearing on the results. The war turned effort and thought to other matters, but peace saw the establishment of the Wildlife Survey Section of the Commonwealth Scientific and Industrial Research Organization, and this was given the task of further trials. In 1950 seven liberations were made in the Murray valley, of which six failed but one succeeded dramatically. This showed a rapid dispersal of the virus, including one movement of 400 miles (644 km) by December and the carrier was attributed to infected mosquitoes, particularly *Culex annulirostris*. The reason for the failure of the pre-war trials, on ground totally unfavourable to mosquitoes, became clear. Experiments showed that, once infected, the mosquito can transfer the disease for up to twenty-five days afterwards and, of great importance to the history of myxomatosis in Britain, any blood-sucking or biting arthropod can act as a carrier.

By the summer of 1951–2 the disease was killing great numbers of rabbits throughout Victoria and New South Wales, with the principal vectors (the scientific term for carriers) being mosquitoes. The spread of myxomatosis by 1952–3 produced some telling statistics. Millions of rabbits died; fatalities in south-east Australia were estimated to reach 80 per cent and the increased value in rural production was valued at £50,000,000. It was thought this was the peak year for mortalities, but the following three years saw very substantial numbers die. By then it was concluded that myxomatosis was permanently established in wild rabbits in Australia and could be expected to bring about a lasting decrease in the rabbit population.

Left to nature it is unlikely that myxomatosis would ever have reached Europe; it had, after all, failed to find its own way here for centuries. Unfortunately from the point of view of the sportsman, the financial rewards of eliminating the rabbit were too great. Whilst many farmers may have desired the result, the action was so dramatic and probably irreversible, that few would have taken the initiative. The dubious honour fell to Armand Delille, a retired physician, who obtained some myxoma virus from Switzerland and caught, innoculated and released two rabbits on his estate in the Department of Eure et Loire, near Paris. This was in June 1952. Within a month most of his rabbits were dead and the disease spread rapidly beyond the boundaries of his estate. By early 1953 it appeared in the south of France, and by the end of the year was reported in nearly every department in the country and in Belgium, Luxembourg, Germany, the Netherlands and Spain. By 1956 it was estimated that the disease had killed 90 per cent of the country's rabbits, and many country people were sharply opposed, with some trying deliberately to spread it and others contain it. It is to be hoped that Monsieur Delille set out with such grandiose ambitions, for if not he must have a troubled conscience. In 1953 some North American rabbits (cottontails), which are only mildly affected by myxomatosis, were imported into France. Rumour places the initiative on United States airmen, presumably motivated by sporting reasons, but the French authorities took a decidedly unsporting view and tried to destroy them. Fearing the same tactic, Britain in 1954 made an Order prohibiting the importation into Great Britain, and keeping of, all species of non-indigenous rabbits.

In passing it is worth noting that, with the exception of a very few Continental hares, no other animals have ever been known to contract myxomatosis, nor have numerous experiments ever succeeded in inducing the disease in other species.

And so we reach the moment when myxomatosis entered Britain. The first outbreak was officially confirmed on 13 October 1953, at Bough Beech in Kent. (Better known among sporting countrymen as the site of an excellent still-water trout fishery.) The infection probably occurred in August or September and a gamekeeper, Mr. Feeke, was the first to report signs of abnormal disease. Quite how the virus reached England we will probably never know. Birds or insects may have been responsible, but my own estimation is that it was a deliberate introduction by man. Certainly once its presence in Britain was known there were many people only too anxious to introduce it into their own area. It requires little more initiative to transport a diseased rabbit across the Channel than across the width of England.

However it came, the fact is that by a fortnight later it had reached Robertsbridge in East Sussex. The authorities enclosed the areas with rabbit-proof netting, killed, so far as they could, all the rabbits within and hoped the disease would die out. At least that is the official history. In practice there may well have been many in authority who regarded myxomatosis as a highly effective and entirely free solution to a long-standing problem. The truth whilst interesting is academic, for in November there were additional outbreaks in Sussex and Kent and, for the first time, Essex. December saw three fresh areas infected, including one in Suffolk.

Up to this point it was believed the principal vector was the mosquito, and as the mosquito over-winters only as eggs or larvae, it was thought the disease, having killed off its immediate victims, might die out. Throughout this winter of 1953–4 an Advisory Committee appointed by the Minister of Agriculture deliberated on whether to confine the disease or take active steps to spread it. Faced with the impossibility of containing it on the one hand and the humanitarian objections to spreading it on the other, the Committee, not surprisingly, recommended doing nothing. Events moved slowly in the first months of 1954, with the disease confined, apart from a case in the Isle of Wight, to the south-east. Then, in May there were isolated outbreaks in Cornwall, Norfolk and Radnor. From a commonsense point of view, is it likely that a disease which we now know to be principally carried by fleas, and which had remained in a relatively small area for nine months, should suddenly make leaps of hundreds of miles by natural causes? I think not. The original slowness may, perhaps, be partly attributed to the nature of the vector, discussed later, but unless I am very much mistaken, man played a major part in this new and startling development. In less than two further months there were 78 outbreaks in 19 counties; in another month it crossed the Scottish border, and by August; just a year after its arrival, there were 255 outbreaks in 61 counties.

My belief that the spread of myxomatosis in Britain was greatly influenced by man is strengthened by the work of Martin in the 1930s, who found that there had to be close contact between rabbits for the disease to pass—even a few inches between cages was an effective barrier. (How much more effective, then, was the gap between Sussex and Cornwall.) Blowflies, for example, could pick up the virus from a sick rabbit but could not transfer it to a healthy one. Nor would rabbits contract the disease from feeding on grass previously grazed by diseased rabbits. Whatever policy the Advisory Committee eventually decided to recommend, it was essential to know how the disease spread, and investigations were quickly begun. Martin's work contradicted the experience gained in Australia and certain parts of Europe, where the failure of attempts to introduce the disease were attributed to the absence of mosquitoes from the localities. If the virus was carried by flying insects how could a barrier of a few inches prove effective? To check the point, in March 1954 six tame rabbits were exposed to natural infection by placing them in hutches in woods near the first outbreak in Kent but—the critical point—the hutches were secured to trees some five feet (152 cm) above the ground. Mosquitoes were abundant in the area in May and June; the local wild rabbits died of myxomatosis, but none of the tame captives.

The mosquitoes were acquitted and the evidence, supported by other experiments, focused on the common European rabbit-flea (*Spilopsyllus cuniculi*), which, significantly, is not present in Australia or New Zealand. Further proof that the disease was being transmitted in this country by a different vector came from a study of the rate of natural spread. At no time did the maximum linear spread exceed 4·1 miles (6·6 km) per month, and from February to November 1954, it only averaged 3·5 miles (5·6 km) but in Australia the disease had been known to spread 3 miles (4·8 km) *per day!*

At this point we can look back to the failure of Sir Charles Martin's attempts to spread myxomatosis among the rabbits of Skokholm Island in 1936. He was convinced the disease was spread by direct contact and therefore made no investigation into possible local insect vectors. Had he done so he would have discovered the remarkable coincidence that Skokholm was, so far as is known, the only place in Britain not to have the rabbit-flea. Had Sir Charles carried out his experiments anywhere else they would probably have been successful and the whole history of myxomatosis in Europe would have been different.

An average rate of natural spread of 3·5 miles (5·6 km) per month could not be reconciled with outbreaks in such far-flung spots as Orkney and Shetland, and public sentiment demanded legislation to stop the artificial spread of myxomatosis. Although enforcing such a restriction was obviously well-nigh impossible, the Government thought it politically expedient to comply, and an amendment to the Pests' Bill made the act an offence. Whether observed or not the measure had no effect upon the spread of the disease, for by 1955 the disease had reached almost every parish in England, Wales and Scotland. The rabbit population had been decimated; the many millions reduced to isolated pockets of survivors, themselves liable to annihilation at any time.

As I explained earlier, my own knowledge of myxomatosis owes much to Thompson and Worden's book. Thorough though this is I was unable to reconcile certain facts; namely, that if the rabbit-flea was the vector why was it that the spread of the disease was much less in the winter, when mosquitoes were absent, than in the summer. Fleas are permanent residents upon their rabbit host so why should the rate of infection vary with the season? Part of the answer lay in a sentence occurring much later in the book, 'Surprisingly little is known of the natural history of the rabbit-flea, the main vector of myxomatosis in Britain, and there is an urgent need for research on this insect.'

Urgent the need might have been, but it was not until 1964 that the definitive work on the subject appeared in the form of a paper by A. R. Mead-Briggs ('The reproductive biology of the rabbit flea *Spilopsyllus cuniculi* (Dale) and the dependence of this species upon the breeding of its host'). At first thought an investigation into the private life of rabbit-fleas might not appear either interesting or appealing—I found it fascinating both for the content and as an illustration of the painstaking thoroughness of a trained scientist at work. The story began when it was found that the normal and successful method of breeding fleas failed when applied to rabbit-fleas. This involved removing the mammal and leaving the cultures in a suitable atmosphere for the duration of the pre-adult stages. Next the more direct technique of releasing rabbit-fleas on to caged rabbits was tried, but again the fleas showed no sign of reproduction. Nor did they respond any more willingly on rats, mice or guinea pigs. Next, 150 female fleas, removed from a shot wild rabbit and gravid in appearance (that is, pregnant) were released onto the head and ears of a domestic rabbit. No eggs appeared and when the fleas were dissected it appeared that 'the larger oocytes in the ovaries were undergoing yolk resorption and subsequent destruction.'

Research continued with the weekly collection and examination of fleas from wild rabbits, and it emerged that the peak of reproductive activity was in February and March, coinciding with the peak breeding season of the rabbit hosts. With this pointer to work on the first successful experimental breeding of rabbit-fleas took place in May 1960, when virgin fleas were released on three female rabbits, two of which were pregnant and one not. After 5 to 8 days the nests of the two pregnant rabbits contained flea eggs and larvae, and examination of the female fleas on the rabbits showed that the ovaries had matured and copulation and impregnation had occurred. The fleas on the non-pregnant rabbit had not been impregnated.

In a nutshell then, rabbit-fleas only breed on pregnant rabbits, or, to quote Mead-Briggs, 'Indeed fleas even when kept for long periods on unmated female rabbits, or on male rabbits never produce any eggs.' Here then is the answer to the question of why myxomatosis spreads more rapidly in the spring than the winter. It is not the emergence of a new generation of mosquitoes but a new generation of fleas unwittingly spreading death to their own hosts, and by virtue of living on them, doing so with more certainty than the roving mosquito.

The more I learn of natural history the more I marvel at the fashion in which every species has evolved to its own advantages. Consider now the story of the birth of a rabbit-flea. If the female flea were to mate and lay her eggs indiscriminately the chances of their survival would be remote. The eggs would fall from the rabbit to the bare floor of the burrow with little chance of finding dried blood, which provides their principal dietary component. Not only does the female restrict her breeding to pregnant females, but she delays until the latter stages when the rabbit will carry her to its nest of grasses and hair. In this ideal environment both male and gravid female fleas can live comfortably, feeding on the young rabbits. The larvae are themselves incapable of piercing the skin of the young rabbits but feed on the faeces of their own parents, formed from part-digested blood.

This account gives no indication of the depth and care of Mead-Briggs's investigations. Consider, for example, the caption to the diagram numbered Fig. 2, 'Diagrammatic optical section of the posterior (proximal) region of an ovariole to show the measurement taken as a criterion of the degree of ovarian maturity. *ep. pl.*, epithelial plug; *fol. ep.*, follicular epithelium; *g, ves.*, germinal vesicle; *l.*, length of proximal oocyte follicle; $oo\cdot_{1}$, $oo\cdot_{2}$, $oo\cdot_{3}$, oocytes 1–3 respectively; *ped.*, pedicel; *y. g.*, yolk granule.' There are many more riches: graphs galore; tables to illustrate such matters as ovarian maturation related to the appearance and size of the proximal oocyte follicles, and even the decline in ovarian maturity among fleas remaining on rabbits after parturition; records of various experiments in which fleas were released into nests and 'subsequently examined to determine whether any ovarian development or impregnation had occurred'. Look behind the cold, scientific description and consider what 'subsequently examined' means in terms of catching and dissecting such difficult subjects as fleas. Eventually the stage is reached of examining the spermatheca of female fleas for spermatozoa! Although I treat the subject lightly I am lost in admiration of the skill, knowledge, equipment and patience involved.

But we wander from our subject of myxomatosis and, in the zest of playing detective in the hunt for the principal vector, have leapt too far ahead in time. We must back-track to 1954 when the Government, aware that myxomatosis could not be controlled, decided to make the most of this opportunity to control permanently rabbit numbers to the point where they could never again become a nuisance. During that year the Pests' Act became law and greatly extended the power of the Minister of Agriculture to control rabbits. Under the Act he may make an order designating an area a rabbit clearance area, which means it must so far as is practical be cleared of wild rabbits. In our legislative measures we British have a pleasant habit of giving those affected a chance to plead their case and the Pests' Act of 1954 is no exception. Before making an order the Minister, or to be more accurate, his representatives, must consult all interested parties, and those affected can make representations. The flaw is that, as with enquiries into proposed motorways and all similar activities where the wishes of the Government impinge on the private citizen, the Government representatives perform as both advocate and judge. As I write there are proposals to ensure that motorway disputes are heard by a completely independent inspector. It may well be that decisions under the present system are perfectly unbiased but under the new proposals they would be known to be, and this, in the context of winning public acceptance, is important. But enough of political dispute—back to more important matters, such as rabbits.

An order may stipulate the manner in which rabbits are to be cleared from a rabbit clearance area and the occupier must comply. If he does not he may be fined, on the basis of Section 98 of the Agriculture Act 1947, a maximum of £25, and if he still fails to comply, a further fine of up to £5 a day. The Minister's powers to ensure rabbit clearance go further than merely fining the occupier and are in fact quite far-reaching. Under the Ground Game Act of 1880 an occupier who has the right to kill rabbits may only authorize one other person to use firearms against them. If the person, usually the owner, having the power to permit the occupier to extend this authorization to more than one refuses such consent, then the Minister may grant permission. Those persons authorized by the Minister can also enter and inspect land at any reasonable time. Nor is the order always expressed in vague and general terms—it may be in positive form instructing the occupier to contain rabbits in certain areas or to destroy specific cover or breeding places.

Although these and the numerous other measures I have not mentioned in the 1954 Pests' Act are mandatory, they were by no means forced on to an unwilling farming community. The majority of landowners were very willing to comply and the principal part played by the Ministry consisted of co-ordination of efforts rather than beating sluggards into action with the ponderous club of the law. Joint effort focused in the formation of Rabbit Clearance Societies, which employed roving teams of rabbit-destroyers, as distinct from catchers, using either gas or ferrets and dealing with each infestation as it arose. This took the burden of rabbit control off busy farmers and landowners, who contributed to the cost in proportion to their acreage, while the Ministry of Agriculture gave encouragement by equalling the local contribution. By 1965 46 per cent of the country areas of England and Wales were covered by Societies, with 670 affiliated to the central body, and by 1968 this had grown to about 800 Societies.

This tactic was an effective way of controlling rabbits. Before myxomatosis the numbers were so vast and their annual expansion through breeding so great that effective control could only be operated in limited areas where the ground was favourable and labour economically available. Once the majority of the rabbits were exterminated the 'fire brigade' could concentrate on local outbreaks and control them before they spread. In spite of this the rabbit literature of the late 1950s was noticeably and sensibly reticent in forecasting the future of the rabbit, although all agreed it would never be exterminated. However, Lockley went so far as to predict that even if myxomatosis died out, or rabbits developed a resistance to it equivalent to that of their South American cousins, they 'are never likely to become a general plague to land-users'. I cannot see why not. Freed from myxomatosis the only thing which would keep their numbers down would be human control, and inflation makes the cost of labour for such purposes increasingly prohibitive.

But will myxomatosis die out or rabbits develop immunity? Here, indeed, is a fascinating question. Certainly those who thought the disease would quickly lose its effectiveness have been proved wrong, for myxomatosis is still a dreadful killer. This summer (1976) I have had a demonstration close at hand. A country railway line runs alongside my property in an embankment, and over the last two years several large burrows have developed on the further bank. From early spring large numbers of young rabbits began to appear, first playing on the embankment close to their holes, and later moving into the field beyond. As the summer progressed so the colony grew, until watching them in the low evening sun I was reminded of my childhood in Norfolk. Early in September we saw the first diseased rabbit and in a very short time the colony was decimated, with the old sickening sights of blind and bemused rabbits slowly dying.

The layman, observing an instance such as this, would conclude the position was unchanged and think pessimistically of the rabbit's future. However, the work of the scientists suggest differently. When myxomatosis first arrived there was a school of thought that believed it would die out because of its own virulence —in other words, it would kill the rabbit population so completely that it would itself die for lack of fresh hosts. In fact if this failed to happen to Australian rabbits, with the faster rate of spread, the risk of a 'self-kill' situation for the disease in this country was remote. In the beginning the survivors from myxomatosis were not those which had recovered but those very few which by sheer chance had never contracted it. If the disease had reached every rabbit it would have exterminated the rabbit and then died out itself. However, viruses can undergo mutation, and this happened, resulting in a more protracted and less severe disease, from which some rabbits not only recovered but derived an active immunity. The first known example in this country occurred in Sherwood Forest, as early as 1955. Other attenuated strains occurred elsewhere, but it was not until 1962 that a scientific survey was conducted. In the autumn of that year 222 myxoma-infected rabbits' carcasses were collected from 85 counties and sent to the Infestation Control Laboratory's Field Research Station at Worplesdon, Surrey. Virus samples were taken from each and groups of six laboratory rabbits were injected. The course of the disease was noted in each rabbit and, if it died, the date of death. (All things being equal the virulence of myxoma virus may be measured by the time it takes to kill.) Now the presumption was that if a similar experiment had been carried out in 1954 the result would have been a kill-rate of 99 per cent plus in all cases. As it was, and without going into great detail, the original highly virulent virus had been replaced by a number of strains of widely differing virulence. Only 4·1 per cent of the samples had sustained the original kill-rate of over 99 per cent. Nearly 40 per cent had dropped to 90–95 per cent, and almost 25 per cent were down to 70–90 per cent. No less than 14 per cent were killing only 50–70 per cent and nearly 1 per cent had a kill-rate of less than 50 per cent.

A rabbit which has once survived will contain antibodies in its blood and will in future survive even the most virulent forms of the disease. Doe rabbits, rendered immune in this way, will pass myxoma-antibodies to their young, which will enjoy a measure of immunity for two to three months after birth. If infected during this period a much greater percentage will recover and will then enjoy a lifetime immunity. (The fact that inherited immunity disappears after a few months is important and a point to which we will return.) In practice, the resistance of rabbits to any given strain of myxomatosis is not constant but varies with individuals, and in time we can expect the force of natural selection to evolve a race of rabbits with increased genetic resistance. This has already occurred in Australia, where, in one area, laboratory tests have shown that the mortality rate of non-immune rabbits to the same strain of virus has fallen from 90 per cent to 25 per cent in only seven years. Taking this trend to its logical conclusion it is easy to forsee our rabbits eventually developing the resistance of the South American rabbits.

The recovery of a rabbit population, after suffering severe losses through myxomatosis, can be more rapid than a brief consideration would suggest. Given an ideal breeding season, with no outside disturbance, even a 90 per cent kill can be recovered in a single year. In fact these ideal conditions are never met, for man and natural predators are invariably a factor, but I quote this figure to underline my earlier point that when myxomatosis loses its strength, I cannot see why the rabbit should not recover its pre-war numbers.

Interestingly those areas where myxomatosis is always present see a lower kill-rate than those where the disease only reappears at lengthy intervals. The reason depends on the earlier point, that a doe rabbit rendered immune by recovering from myxomatosis, can only pass on this immunity to her young for a month or so. If myxomatosis returns yearly then the numbers surviving will be increased by those adults already immune after an earlier recovery. At the same time those very young rabbits enjoying partial immunity through their mother will contract the disease in a mild form, survive, and then enjoy life-long immunity. Finally the colony will have some rabbits which survive through natural resistance. The total of survivors, through one reason or another, will be such as to enable a rapid build-up of numbers to the point where the rabbit-fleas can again transmit the disease quickly. This next bout of myxomatosis will find a good percentage of immune and resistant rabbits and the cycle will continue.

This situation naturally occurs in those areas which for reasons of available cover, food and lack of disturbance favour the rabbit. In less hospitable areas the build-up of numbers is slower and more time elapses before the densities are reached at which fleas become effective vectors. In this extended period many, if not all, of the actively immune adults will have died and the temporary immunity bestowed on some of the young by immune does will have lapsed. Consequently, the kill-rate will be much higher and the greatly reduced population will take a long time to recover its number to a fresh danger level. Once again the extended period will see the death, for various reasons, of those which gained immunity from the last wave of myxomatosis, and once again the kill-rate will be high.

Those readers who are anxious to exterminate, or at least keep to a minimum, those rabbits on their ground should not miss the significance of the foregoing. Immediately after an attack of myxomatosis the population will be greatly reduced and efforts to kill off the survivors will be very unproductive. None the less the elimination of these survivors is critically important for many of them will be both immune and capable of passing on temporary immunity to the next generation. *Delaying* the build-up of numbers is the key factor in ensuring a high kill-rate in the next outbreak of disease.

For those of us who see the rabbit purely as an excellent sporting quarry, it is difficult to sympathize with those who would welcome its extermination. However, seeing the other man's point of view is helped by some cold statistics. In 1951–2, that is just prior to the arrival of myxomatosis, it was estimated that there was an average loss on wheat crops of 1·6 cwt. an acre due to rabbit grazing. The total cost of the rabbit to agriculture was put at £60 million a year. In 1955 damage was neglible and some counties claimed a 15 to 20 per cent increase in production. As usual I view all round figures and unproven estimates with suspicion, for if anyone has an axe to grind, a benefit to be won, or a bias to push further, then estimates, opinions and forecasts glow brightly in the fires of their enthusiasm. This is not to suggest that rabbit damage was not very serious—it was, but it is hard to reconcile some of the statistics. Consider these:

At this time (late 1976), I find it impossible to gather any official opinion on the present rabbit population as against the pre-myxomatosis figures. Occasionally, but very occasionally, there are reports that the population in a small area has reached a pre-myxomatosis level. Usually disease returns and the numbers crash. Many other areas report only a small fraction of the pre-disease level. My own observations, in areas I have known all my life, suggest the *average* levels to be certainly less than half. A personal friend, who has been professionally concerned with rabbits and myxomatosis since the first outbreak, believes the population is running at about 40 per cent of pre-myxomatosis days.

If 40 per cent is a reasonable forecast now, in late 1976, then it was certainly no more in 1974. Yet in that year a survey by the National Farmers' Union estimated that rabbit damage was costing £100 million a year, which, allowing for inflation, about equalled the £60 million pre-myxomatosis level.

How could the same amount of damage be done by only 40 per cent of the rabbits? You see what I mean about statistics!

One last interesting side-issue of myxomatosis remains to be considered, namely the legend of 'bush-rabbits'. There are, so the story goes, a new generation of rabbits which have learnt to live above ground to escape the rabbit-flea and its consequences. To suggest such an assessment of cause and effect by the rabbit is moving into the realms of fantasy, but there is a scientific argument to support the apparent growth of bush rabbit numbers. Where there is really good thick ground cover there have always been rabbits which have lived either entirely or partially above ground. Free from the confinements of a burrow they will have had less contact with their fellows and the relatively immobile rabbit-flea will have had less opportunity to transmit myxomatosis. While this does not assist a growth of numbers, it at least limits the reduction, and in an adult-rabbit-less countryside, any evidence of numbers is construed as growth. Additionally the theory of a new breed of above-ground rabbit has the attractions of being logical and simple to propound. Given many generations of high-kill rate myxomatosis, natural selection might well favour those rabbits which preferred a ground level existence, but at the moment I am sure the answer is simpler—above-ground rabbits are less vulnerable to myxomatosis and therefore more survive.

An interesting but not particularly happy chapter, and it is a pleasure to turn to ferrets and their welfare.

CHAPTER SIX

Ferret Management

The quality of life of all captive or domesticated creatures depends largely upon their keepers, and the lot of the ferret has improved in recent years. Previously they were kept mainly by keepers and agricultural workers who, living hard lives with little time for sentiment, gave the greatest care to the most valuable animals. Ferrets, easily and cheaply bred, came well down the scale and were in some cases neglected to the point of cruelty. There were of course men who held their pugs in great affection but far too many kept them in gloomy cramped hutches, which were cleaned only at lengthy intervals. Feeding was irregular, often consisting of a whole rabbit, whereupon the owner felt his obligation discharged for some days.

Unfortunately such neglect can still be found, and it is a shameful way to treat such friendly, alert little animals, which so amply repay proper attention. However, most ferrets are now kept for sport rather than for rabbit control or profit, and the natural regard with which their owners hold them has brought an automatic improvement in their conditions.

The principles of keeping ferrets do not differ in any way from those for keeping any other animal or, for that matter, children—feed them properly and keep them warm, dry and clean. Observe these rules conscientiously, handle them often, and they will be playful and friendly. (Ferrets, not children.) Our own ferrets obviously enjoy being handled and rush towards any member of the family who approaches their run. This leads conveniently to one of the principles of ferret management which is rarely mentioned, that is the advantage of an outside run. Given the basic principles already listed, there is nothing which can improve their lives so much as the ability to enter the open air at will for a romp or a bask in the sun. Both physically and mentally these alert and vigorous animals benefit enormously from their freedom and, after observing a group wrestling and playing in an open run, it is depressing to think of others permanently confined in a small, dark hutch, However, more of runs later; for the moment let us begin at the beginning with the correct names.

In fact, you may take your pick and still be as correct as the next man, for there seems to be no absolute rule. Sedgwick says the proper terms are hob and jill, but he himself used dog and bitch. However, Parker, in *Elements of Shooting*, states categorically that dog and bitch, buck and doe, and jack (not, be it noted, hob) and jill, are all equally correct. Other writers use whichever couple of names appeals to them without stating a case.

Selecting a ferret from a litter of young is very much a matter of chance, for there can be few people capable of making a reasoned choice from a writhing, tumbling, biting, scratching bundle of minature clowns. Discard any obvious runt, check that the eyes, legs, feet and mouth are in good order and then please your fancy. There is a case for picking the kitten which is most observant of movement or sound, but they vary individually from hour to hour and it is necessary to observe them closely for several days to be sure which, if any, are the more alert.

So far as sex is concerned jills are usually easier to tame. They are also smaller and not as strong as hobs, which fact immediately opens two opposing arguments on working. One person prefers hobs on the ground that, being larger and more ferocious, they are better at driving out rabbits. The other reasons that a persistent jill will still bolt the rabbit but is less able to kill it and then lay up. Personally, I prefer the latter theory. I do not think rabbits are bolted or not according to the strength and ferocity of the ferret, for reasons which will emerge in Chapter 7.

Another objection to jills is the belief that if they are not mated when they come into season for the second time they will die young. As with so many statements about ferrets it is difficult to obtain substantive proof. Writer after writer repeats this as a fact, but none gives any medical reason why it should be so. Perhaps it is true, or it may be that, many years ago, some simple soul had several virgin jills die of unobserved diseases and evolved the theory. Once some writer on rural matters had heard and recorded it, it would be handed on from author to author like religious dogma. The only writer I could trace who claimed personal experience was a Mr. Sam Wilson, writing in the *Gamekeeper and Countryside* magazine, who said his unmated jills 'tended to take ill in the form of paralysis to which they soon succumbed'.

Jill or hob, it is easier to select from adult ferrets than young. One simple rule is to buy from a man who is fond of them. His strain will be tame and friendly, well kept and healthy. Whether you pick a white or a polecat is a matter of personal choice coupled with the fors and againsts I list later. There is a cross between the two which Barkley refers to as grizzly beasts and believes them to be dull, slow creatures. In fairness to grizzlies, we have one and she is as good as her brothers and sisters. Turning again to Barkley, we read, 'When I have the ferret in hand, I first look at its tail and then at its feet, and if these are clean it will do. If on the other hand I find a thin appearance about the hairs of its tail and a black-looking dust at the roots, the ferret goes back into the tub; or if the underside of the feet are black and the claws encrusted with dirt, I will have nothing to say to it, as it has the mange and will be troublesome to cure.'

Playful ferrets are almost always good ones, for the trait requires liveliness and perhaps more intelligence than their staider colleagues. A ferret which bites can, provided it is only a few months old, very probably be taught better manners. Question the owner to find whether it has been much handled or not. If the former, leave it, but if the latter it is almost certainly just a question of gentleness and patience. Just as all Chinese look alike to the Westerner, so to the casual observer is there a similarity among adult ferrets. In fact, they are all different in both character and appearance. If you have a choice of several, and time to spare, don't rush. Watch them for a while, and they will soon become individuals.

Ferrets being professional biters it is wise if, at this early stage, we consider how best to hold them. Never plunge your hand rapidly at a ferret or, in fright, it will bite. Move your hand to it slowly, from a position where the ferret can see it, and run it quietly onto its back. Hold it gently round the shoulders, with the front legs between the first and second fingers. Do not then dangle it like a lifeless sack, but lift it, pass a friendly word or two, stroke its head and tickle its tummy. There is more than sentiment in this performance for a ferret so treated will not be one of those annoying beasts which, after a long wait, peeps out of a rabbit hole and then flees in again at your approach. Whilst a well-tamed ferret, properly handled, should never bite, the occasional nip from a youngster is unavoidable. Fortunately their ability to bite in the first three carefree months is limited.

If you are badly bitten the first problem is to persuade the ferret to let go. Bending one of its feet is strongly recommended but has always seemed to me to suffer two drawbacks. One is the risk of finishing up with a ferret with a broken leg. The other is that it will substitute the hold it has for another in the thing which is hurting its leg. Personally, I have found water most effective as the ferret is so bemused by the strange experience it has no inclination to take a fresh bite. The only problem is the discomfort of wandering around, seeking a tap or stream, with a ferret dangling from one finger.

On the subject of taming, I will quote once more from Barkley, and without shame, for this really is an excellent little book. What fun there must have been in conversing with the man. 'It should be constantly handled till it is quite tame before it is used. Little brothers and sisters will be found useful at this.' Then follows much advice about putting the youngsters and the ferret in a shed together, finishing with the admonishment, 'You had better not be in the way when the children return to their mother or nurse.' In an effort to make amends to Mother, he elsewhere recommends young readers to 'Above all, respect your mother, and show your respect by not taking ferrets or dead rats in your pockets into her drawing-room, and by washing your hands a little between fondling them and cuddling her.'

When ferrets are removed from their normal quarters for work or travel they are liable to be out for some hours, and often in cold weather. Their mode of transport, therefore, warrants some care. Surprisingly, Barkley recommends a canvas bag, principally on the grounds that a carrying box felt like a grandfather clock on his back. It is slightly better than the popular sack, whose sole advantage is the ease with which it may be carried, but from the ferret's viewpoint offers little shelter on cold days or in rain, is hot and stuffy on the rare warm ones, and if stepped on, offers no protection. A light box, built of thin plywood is better in every respect, and the extra trouble of making one with a half-moon back which fits snugly to the body is fully repaid in ease of transport. It needs a wide strap to avoid cutting your shoulder and the size will be determined by the number of ferrets you wish to carry. Two feet in length, a foot broad and nine inches or so high (approximately 61 cm × 30 cm × 23 cm) will take three ferrets comfortably. A removable partition in the centre is useful either to keep a liner from the working ferrets, or to separate the ferrets from nets or other equipment. Ventilation holes should be bored at the top, or a 'window' provided with a grill. Doors are best opening at the top, which gives you a slight advantage over the ferret. The confusion of trying to box two ferrets without decapitating them with the door is eased if each ferret has a separate compartment. Against this is the ferret's love of snuggling up with a companion on cold days. Obviously the box should be well lined with straw. Having provided a decent temporary home for your ferrets, don't spoil the job by omitting the small details later. When not in use hang it in a dry place; change the straw frequently; and when ferreting, don't put it down just anywhere, but pick a dry spot out of the wind.

We move now from temporary to permanent homes. Very few people keep more than a few ferrets nowadays, and hutches are the almost universal solution; but in older times warreners and others who had need of large numbers would have a ferret court. Niblett showed a design for a court to keep fifty ferrets, which measured twelve feet by six feet (366 cm × 183 cm). The sides were of brick or tile and a central division separated jills from hobs. At one end were several sleeping compartments, and the court could either be within another building or outdoors. Various alternative designs have appeared, including, in Harting's *The Rabbit*, an enclosure of planks, set edgewise and held by stakes. This particular description finishes with a comment which so aptly, albeit rather quaintly, sums up the advantages of giving ferrets outdoor freedom that I cannot better it: 'They are thus enabled during the fine weather to gallop about the enclosure, bask in the sun, and breathe pure air, the result being that they remain lively and vigorous, and free from disease.' Logically the more nearly the conditions in which you keep animals approaches their natural way of life the better. However, leaving runs for a moment we will look at hutches. Every keen ferret owner has his own ideas on the ideal hutch, and a study of the various literature immediately throws up numerous differences in the size, number of divisions, positioning of doors and, in fact, just about every possible variable. We find, as we do on so many aspects of ferreting, yet more evidence of the divergence of ideas which occur in a minority activity where circumstances restrict the exchange of ideas.

The one aspect on which all agree is that the hutch or 'cub', as it is sometimes called, must be waterproof. You will presumably build your own hutch (it is all part of the fun of ferrets), and great care should be taken to keep rain out from whatever angle it comes. The roof can be covered with a good quality bitumastic felt, and should have a generous fall. Surprisingly, the design shown in Samuel and Lloyd's *Rabbiting and Ferreting* showed the fall to the front, thereby giving a cramped entrance and the maximum height at the rear where it cannot be utilized. The reverse is best, and do provide a generous overhang so that water running off the roof is well clear of the sides. Horizontal weatherboarding for the vertical faces keeps out driving rain, as does tongue-and-groove boarding. Ordinary flat-edged boarding keeps out neither rain nor draughts.

For two ferrets a minimum internal size should be three feet long (91 cm) by eighteen inches (45·5 cm) deep. This is, I stress, a minimum, and really the bigger the better. A good, workable height is eighteen inches (45·5 cm) at the front falling to fifteen inches (38 cm) at the rear. The hutch should be divided into two compartments, each with a separate door for cleaning, and the division requires a hole no larger than necessary. One compartment is for sleeping, and should be smaller than the other and have a solid wooden door. The other compartment, the 'living'-room, needs a wire netting cover to a framed door, to allow the maximum amount of light and air. To assist cleaning keep the floor completely flat.

This is the most basic form of hutch and where the ferrets will not have access to a run, it is better to lengthen the hutch and form a third compartment which they will use as a lavatory. A convenient arrangement is to have a sliding shutter operated by a rod leading outside, which allows you to confine the ferrets in one area while you work in another. In spite of the natural cleanliness of ferrets it is impossible for the hutch to remain pleasant if they are obliged to conduct their sanitary affairs in it. This is yet another a dvantage of a run, but if circumstances make this difficult then, in fairness to the ferrets, you must discipline yourself to a regular cleaning programme. The ferrets will consistently use one corner of the open compartment and holes should be bored in the wooden floor to allow liquid to drain. Some people recommend a floor of wire netting, but this quickly clogs and is no better. The best arrangement is a tray of sand, changed daily. The main area should be cleaned out at least three times a week, but the sleeping area less often. Occasionally a dusting of insect powder along the floor, corners and angles is advisable.

It is pointless to devote a great deal of time to making a good hutch and then site it badly. Obviously it should stand out of the wind and face south to enjoy the sun. An excellent arrangement is for it to be indoors in the winter in a shed or other building, but near a window, and out in the fresh air in the summer. In really hot weather an outdoor hutch, exposed to the full sun, needs a cover of some sort to deflect the heat, and particularly so when there is a litter of young. If, regrettably, you will not be providing a run, there is no point in bending unnecessarily, and the hutch should have legs which elevate it to the most convenient height. In this case a 'skirt' of timber about a foot (30 cm) deep and nailed onto the legs will reduce draughts on the underside of the floor. If the hutch is outdoors in freezing conditions cover it with sacks, including most of the open compartment door.

As a final alternative, consider Niblett's suggestion of an old potato barrel. It is, he admits, a makeshift, but I liked the advice on cleaning it out: 'Invert the barrel—the ferret or ferrets having been previously removed.' Very wise.

The experts differ on the form of litter to be used. Sedgwick advises straw or hay for bedding and straw or sawdust for the run. Samuel and Lloyd merely refer to a soft litter and sawdust and other writers are equally open-minded, but Barkley is emphatic that only wheat-straw should be used. Barley or hay will, he states, give ferrets mange in a few days. I do not know if he is right, but sawdust is unsuitable for a run where feeding takes place. Ferrets rarely feed from their dish, but select a morsel and gallop away to some secret corner. In the process they often drop the food which gains a coat of sawdust. Straw is cleaner. This habit of secret eating should be remembered when cleaning out, as stores of elderly unsavory tit-bits may be found hidden. This is an indication of over-feeding.

I will not weary you by once more advocating a run beyond listing one more advantage—there is much pleasure to be gained from watching ferrets at play. Or nearly always. Last winter we were adopted by a robin with a wounded wing. He could fly but only just, and having the wit to realize we were a soft touch, hung around the kitchen. One awful morning my youngest daughter and I went to feed the ferrets and the robin fluttered into the run and started to peck. We shouted and rushed forward, but too late! Chiff and Chaff, the polecats, stared in disbelief, then rushed in from opposite sides. The robin died in a second but the tug-of-war went on for some time.

The last aspect to cover before leaving the question of quartering is the matter of numbers per cub or hutch, and the criterion must be what is best for the ferrets rather than convenient for us. Many experienced ferreters believe that a liner should be kept alone to encourage the qualities of selfishness and aggressiveness desirable for the performance of its particular task. Beyond observing that some humans of my acquaintance have achieved these characteristics without being imprisoned in solitary confinement, I have no particular view. Certainly ferrets are very gregarious creatures, loving to live and play with others and life is better for them if they have a companion. Two, then, should normally be a minimum per hutch, but four is as many as can conveniently be managed. Normally hobs and jills should be kept separately unless you wish to breed, when the lucky pair should be placed in a separate hutch.

Next we come to feeding and with it yet more disagreement among the authorities. Part of this concerns the question of feeding prior to working, but this can be left to the relevant chapter while we consider, now, the day to-day routine. Just what uten-

1. Rabbit's eye view of a ferret

2. Ferret hutch with permanent access to an open run—an important feature in maintaining the health and fitness of ferrets

3. Happiness is a warm mouse

4. Ten-day-old ferret kitten—a rare sight as most breeders do not see the young until they are three to four weeks old

5. Ten-day-old ferret kittens

6. A jill ferret carries her kitten back to the nest

7. A remarkable demonstration that well-tamed jill ferrets do not object to their kittens being handled

8. At fourteen days this kitten has learnt to drink

9. A fine four-week-old litter—alert and active with excellent coats

10. A young wild rabbit of approximately six weeks

11. A rabbit, surprised in the open, freezes

12. Young rabbit in early morning sun

13. A remarkable photograph of a rabbit, caught in mid-leap

14. Severe myxomatosis, causing the eye-lids to swell and cause blindness

15. Two of the author's sons ferreting in the Hebrides

16. Entering a ferret under a mid-winter sun in Cambridgeshire

17. With the rabbit well bagged in a purse net and a ferret attached, one of the author's sons has a problem to untangle

18. Deep winter is a good time for ferreting as the undergrowth has died back and visibility is good

19. The author's third son enters a ferret in a Surrey hedgerow

20. Rabbits bolting between holes call for snap shooting—this one has been missed over its back

21. Rough shooting for rabbits among bracken on a Skye hillside

22. A well-set net—the mesh has been well stretched over the hole; ample slack has been gathered around the edges; the 'bag' is away from the hole; and the peg is driven in against the pull of a bolting rabbit

24. A lurcher puppy—the favourite dog of the old-time poacher

23. (*Left*) A man-trap of unknown date but still murderously effective

25. A fine specimen of a lurcher

sils they are fed in is of no great consequence, as long as two rules are observed. Firstly, and for obvious reasons, they should be kept constantly clean. Here the vital word is 'constant'. A quick wipe round with a handful of straw will not do. You will not go far wrong if you apply to your ferrets the same standards of cleanliness you seek for yourself. Secondly, the utensils should be heavy so they are not easily knocked over.

Feeding divides into the questions of how often and with what. On the matter of frequency advice varies between Samuel and Lloyd at twice daily and a Hampshire friend of mine at once a week! The latter having given up keeping ferrets I was spared the need to remonstrate, but this practice was once not uncommon. The technique was to chuck a rabbit or some other sizable meal into the hutch and then ignore the animals for several days. It owes more to idleness than any genuine belief that it is best for the ferrets. Informed opinion varies between once or twice a day. My own view is that once a day more nearly approximates to natural conditions, although a jill suckling young will need a constant supply of milk. Quantity must also play a part, for there is really no difference between two small meals and one large one. Keep an eye on their waistlines and vary the amount to keep them neither too fat nor too skinny. Ferrets, as I mentioned earlier, have a habit of hiding tit-bits, presumably to keep them from their companions with the object of clearing the pieces up later. However, if you are over-feeding these will be left and become foul.

The question of what to feed leads us to the great bread and milk debate. Many thousands of ferrets have lived their lives almost entirely on this diet, with their owners staunchly contending it was best for them. On the other hand, most of the more thinking authorities argue that bread and milk is unnatural and flesh is correct. Logic entirely supports the latter view. So do I, but before arguing in its favour it is worth recording that ferrets really do like bread and milk. It is noticeable with ours that when given both they will secrete away the milk-saturated bread before turning to the meat.

Harting says categorically, 'The most suitable food is bread and milk, or porridge (not too wet, and by no means allowed to become sour), varied occasionally with fresh meat.' This statement ignores the simple fact that the ferret is a carnivorous animal and should, therefore, eat flesh. It is, of course, perfectly true that a ferret will survive apparently perfectly well on bread and milk but the evidence of its evacuations suggests that its stomach is none too happy on the diet. Fed on flesh the faeces are normal, whereas on bread and milk it lives in a state of permanent scour. Niblett felt strongly on the subject and quoted Mr. Lascelles Carr as saying, 'I give my ferrets nothing but animal food in the shape of fresh-killed birds, rats, or rabbits, or scraps of butcher's meat. This with a constant supply of fresh water is their daily diet, and they appear to enjoy perfect health. They come to hand with the greatest freedom, are free from all ferocity, are always ready for work, and can work as long and as cleanly as any ferrets I have seen.' Later he quoted another authority, 'It is a great mistake to feed ferrets upon an entirely bread and milk dietary. The ferret is a carnivorous animal, and in our opinion is never so healthy or so active as when subsisting chiefly upon a flesh dietary. We have tried both over a series of years, and we are convinced in our own mind which is the better food. Try both for a time with working ferrets and see which gives the better results. When we feed our ferrets on bread and milk we noticed that the faecal discharges were always more or less watery and evil-smelling, and both adults and young (the latter more particularly) were subject to 'scours'. They were also far from active even though kept in roomy, well-ventilated and scrupulously clean hutches. They, moreover, worked but in very half-hearted manner. No sooner, however, were they given a few freshly-killed birds or a few fowls' heads from the poulterers, etc., than they underwent a change and seldom were sick or sorry, and worked with the desired will and freedom.' I quote these two passages at length because, although dated by the somewhat stilted formality of their phrasing, they give the opinions of two people well worth listening to.

Several books recommended feeding ferrets with rats but Barkley said many old rat-catchers always cut off the tail in the belief there was poison in it. He quoted one old fellow as saying, 'Bar the tail—I allus bars the tail—there's wemon in the tail.' But Barkley adds, 'There may be "wemon" in it, but if there is, it won't hurt the ferrets, for they never eat it or the skin.'

On balance the best course is to feed mainly with flesh, filling in with bread and milk (the milk diluted 50/50 with water) when flesh is not cheaply available. A deep freeze obviously helps. When rabbits are plentiful we prepare them in small parcels, each containing a day's supply, and then draw as needed. There are many other sources of flesh which you may previously have failed to note, including road casualties, such as squirrels, small birds and pheasants too badly mangled for the personal pot. Do not pluck or de-fur too much; to do so presents the ferret with an unnatural meal, and the tussle involved in getting at the flesh also provides interest and exercise. However, make a point of removing bones and other debris after a few hours before they become foul.

On the subject of feeding Barkley raises an interesting point over the popular belief that ferrets suck the blood of their victims; a theory based on the sucking noise emitted by the ferret once it has a good hold. An examination of both the throat of the ferret and the wound of the victim will not usually show much blood. Barkley contends that a ferret sinks its teeth so deep that the noise comes from its efforts to breathe.

Harting, who supports the practice of feeding only once in twenty-four hours and keeping them in runs, recommended whistling at meal times, when the ferrets would rapidly learn to respond.

There is a quite common belief that ferrets do not need or like water, and that the moisture contained in a bread and milk diet is sufficient. This is quite wrong and a bowl of fresh water should be available at all times. The rate at which it is consumed in hot weather is ample proof of their need. In fact, ferrets enjoy water externally as well. On really hot days we will sometimes train the lawn sprinkler on a corner of the run, when the ferrets will dance in and out of the spray with obvious enjoyment. Sedgwick took the contrary view, that ferrets dislike water, but this seems to have been based on their reaction to a ditch of cold water in winter. Not, I feel, a fair test.

Ferrets are by nature very clean animals but whether they can observe this instinct depends upon their owners following a strict cleaning discipline. With an adequate run the problem is immeasurably eased, but without this the open area of the hutch will need cleaning every few days—more frequently in hot weather. The interior of the hutch should be disinfected regularly, and the ferrets themselves need an occasional dusting with insect powder. However, never do this to a jill with young. If you should find a tick with its head firmly embedded in a ferret never attempt simply to pull it out. The head will remain under the skin and possibly fester. Wet the tick thoroughly with either iodine or a mixture of olive oil and paraffin in the proportion of 8 to 1. Several wettings over a period of a day or so will be necessary, but the tick will soon die and fall away.

Observing all the principles of management set out in this chapter should ensure that your ferrets live comfortably and contentedly, and the business of looking after them flows peaceably along. Until, that is, the time to breed arrives when a fresh set of problems arises.

The first step is selecting a suitable hob. Obviously it must be far enough removed from the jill to avoid any risk of in-breeding. It is also essential to pick a hob which is known to be a good worker, yet of a pleasant disposition. There is no pleasure in owning fierce, bad-tempered creatures which bite freely. Size must be taken into account, depending upon whether, for reasons which will emerge later, you want large, small or medium sized ferrets. The jill also should be selected for her good qualities, although opinions differ on precisely what the good points of a ferret are. Some favour blunt-headed, thick-set ferrets on the grounds that they are strong. Niblett disliked this type and favoured 'a sharp muzzle; long, lithe, but withal muscular body, set on clean muscular legs; and a good sweep in the turn of the animal's form are the main points of excellence.' My view is that temperament, a willingness to work and the rare quality of never laying up for long are of far greater importance than physical appearance. Indeed, if I had a ferret that never laid up I would breed from it, were it cross-eyed and knock-kneed.

With breeding, as with so much else, we find various authors at variance. In the days when wild polecats were more common it was often believed that crossing a jill with one produced excellent kittens. Harting was emphatic that 'there can be no doubt that a cross with the latter [polecat] improves the breed materially, for the young are stronger in constitution, and work quicker and longer than ordinary ferrets, which after two years get slow and lazy.' Niblett disagreed, 'We do not believe in the supposed merit of the first cross between the ferret and the polecat.' Whichever is correct the present status of the polecat makes the truth, for us, a matter of academic interest only.

Mating polecat ferrets never produces a white kitten, nor do white crosses produce even the occasional polecat. However, crossing a polecat with a white produces a rather nondescript, in-between, ferret.

Jills come into season in the period March to May, their condition being obvious from the swollen vulva. Unless mated this state may continue for several months. The actual mating would seem, judging from the noise, to be a violent affair. It is difficult to be more factual as the cardinal rule is to effect the introduction and leave them alone. Consumed with curiosity I did once open the bedroom door to offer the happy couple a bowl of milk, reasoning that after twenty-four hours of nuptials they would need it. He, a large amiable creature and a groom imported for the occasion, had his teeth in the back of the bride's neck and was just dragging her across the floor. I proffered the drink and he stood motionless for several seconds until, man-like, his stomach won and he came to the milk.

Our own practice has been to leave the pair together for a day or so, but several writers recommend just two short visits on consecutive days.

The period of gestation is six weeks, give or take a day or so either side, and the jill can remain with her usual companions until a week or so before her babies are born. One man, writing in the *Shooting Times* in 1976, told of keeping a number of ferrets in a large building among straw bales and letting the jills have their litters in the commune. Whilst interesting, and quite believable knowing the character of the ferret, it would be unwise unless you had an excess of space and a keen mind for experiment.

For once all the authorities are agreed on one thing—under no circumstances should you open up the hutch to look at the youngsters or the jill may kill and eat her young. Niblett suggests the kittens may be peeped at once they are four to six weeks old; Sedgwick calls for privacy up to five or six weeks; and Harting decrees waiting until the young appear in the outside compartment.

Assuming the various writers have heeded their own advice it is not surprising that they are wrong over the question of when the kittens open their eyes, with Sedgwick saying they 'are blind for the first six weeks of their life'; Niblett stating, 'At six weeks old the young see'; Samuel and Lloyd claiming, 'their eyes opening after about six weeks' and Harting wisely keeping quiet on the subject. In fact the eye slits are beginning to split at three weeks and are usually fully open by four.

The belief that jills kill their young if the nest is inspected almost certainly has foundation in fact, and you would be wise to leave it alone. However, in my case, the object was not just breeding ferrets but discovering the truth and we have always investigated every nest at seven days. (The actual birth is obvious, as the young begin to squeak immediately.) In no case have we had a jill kill her young, or even show the slightest degree of concern, but then it must be remembered that these are exceptionally well-handled and very tame ferrets.

The number in the litter will usually vary between six to ten, with jills having their first litter at the lower end. There is absolutely nothing that should be done, other than to keep them quiet and ensure the mother is well fed. She will require meals at least twice a day, and diluted milk should be provided ad lib. As I write, in the summer of 1976, we have just finished the exceptional three-month heatwave and I hear reports of numerous litters failing to survive. I am sure the exceptional heat was the cause, and I attribute our own successful raising of two litters to taking from our coarse-fishing sons their large umbrellas and erecting these over the hutches as sun shades.

One particularly interesting fact was that we found, on several occasions, one of the jills dragging the milk bowl by her teeth to the entrance of the inner compartment. Presumably as the kittens were too young to come to the milk she was taking the milk to them.

Our experience again runs counter to others on the question of when the young leave the nest. Samuel and Lloyd say eight weeks, Niblett six weeks and Sedgwick at least six weeks. In fact they are very mobile, although still blind, at three weeks, dragging themselves into the outer compartment, only to be picked up by the scruff of the neck by the jill and taken back to the nest. This she does assiduously until she judges they are capable of looking after themselves, at about four weeks, when she permits them the full run of the hutch and, in our case, the outdoor run. From an early age she shares her food with the kittens, running into the nest with tit-bits and reappearing immediately. There is no question but that ferrets make excellent mothers, and the sight of one lying full length with a youngster on each teat, although seen by very few people, is a picture of contentment. It is very satisfying to have so gained the confidence of the jill that you can place your hand in the nest and fondle both her and the kittens with no reaction from her except pleasure.

Several writers have advised that if you want large ferrets you should cull all but two or three of the kittens at an early age. Our experience is that the fewer the larger certainly works in the early stages. Of the two litters born this year one had eight and one four. The kittens in the smaller litter were nearly twice the size of the larger by five weeks, but I am by no means sure this difference would endure into adult life. As with humans those on lesser rations may rapidly catch up once the pickings are easier.

From as early as three weeks the young will begin to lap milk from a bowl and by four to five weeks are feeding vigorously. Here again our experience conflicts with that of other writers who suggest this stage is not reached until several weeks later. As the performance of our kittens has been constant with various litters, either other observers in their anxiety not to disturb the nest have failed to note the earlier feeding attempts, or our kittens are unusually advanced. The latter is most unlikely.

A change of feeding bowl is necessary at some point in this stage to avoid the kittens drowning. In the first phase it needs to be high-sided to avoid their crawling in and drowning. However, this prevents their drinking and once they have enough strength to escape should they fall in, a lower-sided bowl should be substituted.

Although there is no reason why 'our' strain should be any different, I am tempted to think they are not normal by a passage in Sedgwick's *The Young Shot*, which reads, on the subject of ten-week-old ferrets, 'the young ferrets may now be allowed to crawl over the hand that feeds them.' At ten weeks ours are not so much kittens as mini-wolves, and placed on the hand would waste no time in crawling but begin to devour it. By this age they are alert, vigorous, and hell for everyone concerned—not least their mother who, exhausted by rearing this bunch of hell-hounds, is inevitably involved in the free-for-alls that take place at frequent intervals. Do not be depressed if the ferret or ferrets you have elected to keep sink needle-sharp teeth into you at every opportunity. It is their natural instinct and there is no reason why they should not be completely tamed. The solution is frequent handling, and the sooner this can start, often at about four weeks of age, the better. Separating the litter to their various future homes helps—watching a healthy litter of young ferrets makes it easy to understand the phenomenon of mob violence! The age at which the kittens can be weaned obviously varies from litter to litter. A litter small in numbers but comprising well grown, vigorous youngsters can be separated as early as seven weeks, but in a large litter the smaller youngsters should be left until eight to ten weeks. Once weaned they need feeding three or four times a day, and particular care should be taken over cleanliness of the utensils and the hutch for this is a vulnerable age for illness.

It is unlikely you will wish to keep more than one or two of the youngsters and I do appeal to you to take care that the remainder go to good homes. We will never release a ferret without enquiring into the experience and attitude of the potential owner. Some are simply undergoing a passing interest, others have no idea how to keep a ferret properly, and some, the worst, give an impression of indifference to its welfare. If in doubt refuse to sell. At the present time an advertisement in the *Shooting Times* will bring a host of enquiries.

You will sometimes hear people talk about training ferrets, but this is a rather grand description of a necessarily limited operation. I do not believe that any ferret ever born knowingly chased a rabbit from its burrow with the object of driving it to its owner. Ferrets follow their natural instinct of pursuing rabbits in an effort to kill them for food. In an effort to escape, the rabbits usually bolt—it is as simple as that, and training is really only helping the ferret to develop its natural instincts. In fact it would do this anyway, and our efforts should centre, not upon teaching it to do something it will do anyway but upon training it not to do two instinctive things. The first, and most important, is not to bite us.

The training for this, as I have mentioned, is frequent handling and this also helps in the second area, which is teaching the ferret not to draw back when it has emerged at the entrance to a hole and you advance to lift it. Particularly with young ferrets, the unfamiliar surroundings of the burrow and the excitement of the scent and possibly contact of a rabbit, will have made it jumpy and excited and the appearance of a vast human form bearing down will cause it to dart back into cover. This is annoying and time-wasting, the more so if you have already been waiting some time, and training a ferret to the point where it not only suffers you to pick it up but actively seeks contact pays dividends. In Chapter 8 I deal in detail on the matter of introducing a ferret to its work.

Given proper treatment ferrets are healthy creatures with good powers of recuperation. A friend of mine once found a large hob wandering on Headley Heath with a dreadful wound on the head and partly scalped. My guess is the owner had been digging for it, accidentally struck it with the spade and left it for dead. It was treated and made a complete and rapid recovery. Nicholas Everitt, writing in 1897, takes a much more pessimistic view of the healthiness of ferrets, beginning his chapter on Ailments and Diseases with 'Delicate by nature, delicate to handle, delicate in their physical capacities'.

In spite of this beginning we must pay regard to him, for in the literature of ferrets and ferreting very little can be found on the subject of the diseases of the ferret and their treatments. Niblett devotes a short chapter to the matter and Samuel and Lloyd also go into some detail, although their comments so closely follow Niblett that it is difficult not to believe they have relied almost entirely on this minor classic. As Niblett wrote well before the last war, the only available advice on ferret diseases takes no account of modern veterinary advances.

Ferrets are susceptible to distemper in the same way as dogs, rabbits and other animals, and as it is highly contagious it is important to spot the symptoms, isolate the victim and call a vet, before it spreads to all your stock. Even then you may be too late, but treatment can, at least, start at an early stage. The first signs are a watery discharge from the eyes and nostrils, which rapidly thickens and turns yellow. The breathing deteriorates, becoming noisy, and the animal coughs frequently in an effort to clear the congestion. Vomiting and diarrhoea follow. Other symptoms are loss of appetite and emaciation.

A variety of treatments are suggested by various authors. Everitt, true to his original pessimism, begins by suggesting that the best treatment for severe cases is to put them down. This apart, his principal remedy was to bath the ferret with a teaspoonful of 'Condy's Fluid', diluted in a pint of warm water, taking care to wash all the pus from eyes and nose. There appears no scientific reason why this should be successful and any recovery is more likely to be due to the secondary advice, to place the patient in a warm, dry hutch. As an alternative, he mentions cod-liver oil, although expressing doubts about its effectiveness. Had I been one of Everitt's ferrets I would have preferred the disease to afflict my head seriously, for, in place of cod-liver oil, my diet would have become beef tea, milk, cream mixed with yolk of eggs and a little port wine.

Niblett recommended aspirin in 2½ g doses, dissolved in milk or sprinkled on flesh, twice or thrice daily. Samuel and Lloyd updated this to T.C.P., 10 to 20 drops in a dessert-spoonful of milk, once daily. Both recommended sprinkling the floor of the cub with an equal mixture of eucalyptus oil and beechwood creosote, as an inhalant. Neither the aspirin nor the T.C.P. are likely to do much good, and a vet will probably administer an antibiotic and possibly some serum to knock out the secondary bacteria and let the animal itself get over the virus. If it can, that is. Even with modern treatment distemper is still a killer.

In fact, it is quite likely that ferrets can be vaccinated against distemper and if you are interested in this preventive measure your vet will be able to give you advice.

Mange, which is caused by mites, is another source of trouble. Niblett says there are two forms, the Sarcoptic and the Follicular, of which the former is the more common, much more contagious and transferable to man and other animals. The disease can be contracted not only by contact with other ferrets, dogs, foxes, or even man, but by using infected containers such as hutches or sacks. It may appear on the underside of the feet, when it is often regarded as foot-rot, or on the body. Where the infection occurs the skin is moist and smells badly. The old remedy was one part of sulphurated lime lotion to nine parts of olive oil, this rubbed in every other day. Samuel and Lloyd suggest a more modern variation of one part sulphur, one part coal tar, and ten parts vegetable oil.

More effective proprietary ointments are now available and my vet suggests that it should be possible to treat ferrets orally, as is now done with cats and dogs. This would obviously be quicker and less messy. Whatever method is used the bedding should be burnt regularly and the hutch disinfected.

Another problem caused by parasites is ear canker, the effect being the same as with dogs and cats suffering in a similar fashion. Niblett gives a detailed and somewhat horrific description of the development of the disease if left unchecked, claiming that it frequently kills young ferrets and causes major discomfort to adults. Fortunately the cure is straightforward and effective. The old remedy was composed of mercurial ointment, carbolic acid and olive oil, but there are now several proprietary ointments which should act faster and save lengthy preparation. Once again there is little point in treating the animal without thoroughly disinfecting the quarters.

A ferret which eats excessively but remains thin and generally in poor condition may have worms. Areca nut was the old remedy and, of the various ways of administering it, Everitt's was the most pleasant (for the ferret, that is). He mixed freshly grated areca nut with kamala or pure santonine and wrapped the powder in balls of butter. Nowadays there are various very effective worming powders, although the manufacturers' instructions do not extend to ferrets and you should take a vet's advice over the quantity administered.

In fact that advice, to consult a vet, should be your standard procedure whenever a ferret is obviously unwell for no known reason. If you had no regard for ferrets you would not be reading this book, and by not seeking qualified advice you take the risk that the ferret may suffer unnecessarily and could even die through an illness which could have been treated successfully.

A ferret should have a life of five to six years, although many of them fail to live a normal span, theirs being a hazardous profession. We should do what we can to make their short lives as comfortable as possible.

CHAPTER SEVEN

Downfalls of the Rabbit

If rabbits could reason they would, no doubt, feel a sense of grievance that while they are content to lead peaceful lives, most of the men and many of the creatures with whom they come in contact are intent on their downfall. The motive may vary from food, be it for the cottager's pot or the fox's young, to the protection of crops, but all are combined single-mindedly in their pursuit. This never-ceasing contest between the rabbit, depending for survival upon the twin advantages of a subterranean existence and a high breeding rate, and its adversaries, displaying in the case of natural predators speed, strength and savagery and in man intelligence, has produced a range of situations and circumstances well worth recording.

While modern methods are effective, some earlier ideas deserve mention for their ingenuity. I mention elsewhere Louis Pasteur's idea of spreading chicken cholera bacillus by introducing it to the vegetation of rabbit runs and hoping it would spread by urine falling on to grazing areas. Another scientific, as distinct from purely physical, method of control, which appeared in the *Agricultural Gazette* of 1844, was to confine rabbits on straw bedding with a 'mangey' dog. After sufficient time had elapsed for the rabbits to have contracted mange they were to be released into the countryside to infect others. No doubt one of the obstacles was finding a dog which not only suffered from mange but was prepared to live peacefully with rabbits. Another idea from the same period was to sow rape which, when eaten by young rabbits in wet weather, would, it was claimed, give them pot-bellies and cause their demise through a liver disease. The middle of the nineteenth century seems to have been a fertile period for rabbit control ideas for, again in 1844, the *Agricultural Gazette* reported that market gardeners were getting rabbits intoxicated and then clubbing them to death in their drunken stupor. The procedure was apparently to soak such crops as parsley in rum or brandy, which leads me to wonder whether the *Agricultural Gazette* was not having its journalistic leg pulled.

Some earlier sufferers from rabbits gave up any hope of eliminating them and settled for the lesser target of deterring them. William Boutcher in his *A Treatise on Forest Trees* (1775) suggested that as hares liked eating laburnum and beatrefoil so much, an ample supply should be planted to entice them from other plants. Three years later Francis Forbes wrote *The Improvement of Waste Land* suggesting the practice could provide permanent protection from rabbit damage. Early in the next century the Board of Agriculture's report for Derbyshire suggested a change of emphasis. Instead of offering a species of tree as a sacrifice to detract the rabbit from wanted species, the more direct approach was recommended of only growing those trees the rabbit actually disliked, the least attractive being the sycamore.

Other deterrent methods were fascinating in their ingenuity, although unattractive in composition. It was common practice to rub the stems of saplings and trees with a mixture of dung and lime; and an alternative was *assa foetida* boiled in dung juice and applied to stems or crops. Cobbett reported the use of tanners' ooze mixed with lime, the latter presumably used as a medium. Tar was very popular and apparently effective. Cobbett also wrote of the use of a mixture of the oils of aniseed, thyme and spirits of tar. Much correspondence appeared in the agricultural press on the subject with one man advocating sulphur spread on dahlias and another suggesting the chemical merely made them more tasty.

Perhaps the most revolting, which in this context means best, mixture was published in the *Field Club*. Take:

One spadeful of hot slaked lime
One spadeful of clean cow dung
Half spadeful of soot
One handful of flowers of sulphur

The whole was then mixed into a thick paste with water and cow urine, which, to quote a favourite saying of a contemporary disc jockey, should soften your cough.

Interesting as deterrents are it is death rather than discouragement which is the concern of this chapter. Ferreting, of course, enjoys a separate chapter but two variations of this method deserve mention. Harting wrote of bolting rabbits by burning a fuse in the burrow, recommending the product of a Messrs. Brunton and Co., of the Cambrian Safety Fuse Works at Wrexham. He quotes *The Field* of November 1892 as reporting that, using these fuses, six Guns shot 1,027 rabbits in one day at Weald Hall, Brentwood, Essex, and the next day shot 405 on the same beat. Sheail has unearthed bizarre substitutes for ferrets from the *Zoologist* of 1844. Fishermen in the Isle of Wight would fix the end of a candle to the back of a king crab, light it, push it into a burrow and wait for the rabbits to flee before this strange monster. Crabs and also lobsters were similarly used in Seaton, Devon, and known as sea ferrets. Gypsies in the Chilterns are supposed to have used the same method, but substituting a large toad for the crab. All very ingenious, but it is not surprising that ferrets retained their popular lead.

A simpler and much more effective technique was practised in the Isle of Caldey in Pembrokeshire. Enclosures containing good grazing were constructed so that rabbits could enter through holes along the base of stone walls. These were left open until a good number of rabbits were present every night, when the holes would be plugged and the imprisoned rabbits dealt with at daylight next day.

Of all the instruments devised by man's ingenuity in pursuit of the rabbit the snare is probably supreme. During its relatively brief reign the gin, calling for less skill, was more effective, but the snare was probably devised when one of our early ancestors first found some unfortunate animal accidentally caught up in a tangle of undergrowth. Like the wheel it has the merit of simplicity and requires but the briefest description. A running noose of flexible wire is supported in position by a slender stick and attached by a cord to a peg in the ground. If properly positioned in the path of a rabbit the victim will, depending upon its speed, either break its neck outright, strangle itself by struggling or lie quietly until dispatched. This description simplifies a difficult art as fully as saying that music can be produced by pressing the keys on a piano.

Snares cannot, of course, be set haphazardly but must be on rabbit runs. Often it is necessary to avoid an open field for fear of catching stock or a dog by the leg. Poachers, as we will see from chapter 10, also avoid open areas, preferring to operate in woods and thick hedges which allow them to come and go unseen. Thick cover also renders a snared rabbit less conspicuous. Spotting a run is easy but greater skill is required to identify the regular impressions made as the rabbits bound along on the same landing places. Most authors had or have their own firm ideas on snare setting and the position of the snare in relation to the impact mark is important. Consider, for example, Tennyson, in *Rough Shooting* (1938), 'A snare set just a fraction in front of one of these dents cannot fail to take the rabbit when his head shoots forward on landing.' Excellent advice as long as the rabbits always run the same way! Sedgwick in *The Young Shot* is more sensible advising that the snare be set in the indentation. Sedgwick, ultimately the editor of the *Shooting Times* and well known for his writings and the name of Tower Bird, had a great many country jobs and wrote from practical experience. Certainly he snared a great many more rabbits than most authors who, like me, mastered the art for fun and then stopped. When setting large numbers he advocates placing them in straight lines for convenience of visiting and removing the catch.

The wire or noose is usually made of several strands of flexible brass wire and the ring which assists it to draw tight is called the thimble. The wire is attached to the peg by a cord and the length and thickness of the peg will vary with local soil conditions. The slender stick which holds the noose in position is sharpened at one end for thrusting into the ground and split at the other to allow the wire to be wedged into it. Popularly this stick is known as a tealer, teeler or pricker. Old countrymen recommended cutting the head of the tealer at an angle and facing the angle away from the run to prevent rabbits seeing the white flash. My good friend Charlie Swan, and Ministry of Agriculture rabbit expert, carried out some snaring trials and, for marking purposes, peeled the fifth tealer completely. He found the snares attached to these very obvious supports caught slightly more than the unpeeled tealers.

Every snarer has his own fixed views on the shape of the noose, the size, the height it is set above ground, the angle of the tealer and other aspects. The fact that men with different techniques all catch rabbits proves that these differences are not critical, although obviously some methods will be more effective than others. Pear-shaped nooses are the most popular, although logically the best shape is a circle. Presumably long experience showed a pear-shape 'drew' better than a circle. Part of the secret of a quick, smooth-drawing noose is to have it free of any kinks or irregularities. This is easily done by drawing it through the cleft in the tealer, although Harting recommended carrying a small piece of wash-leather for the purpose. (He is also very pernickety on removing human scent and recommends washing well and then running the hands in mould taken from the area in which the snares are to be set.) As to height, the general consensus is that the bottom of the noose should be the height of the knuckles above the ground, although Tennyson adds the thumb as well.

Snares may of course, and also provided your activities have the blessing of the farmer or owner, be set at any time. (Although Harting reports an old keepers' belief that 'Snares set in the morning catch twice as many rabbits as those set in the evening or afternoon, because the scent gets off and evaporates during the day, whereas in the evening the dews fall and preserve the scent freshly all night, thus warning off the rabbits.') What is more important is the time you visit them. Old-time commercial snarers were motivated by the need to remove a snared rabbit as quickly as possible so that the snare could be set to work once more. Modern snarers who operate mainly for sport should have the humane aspect well in mind and make regular visits, preferably every dawn to dispatch any snared rabbit still alive.

The Field of 19 December 1891 reported the first 'humane rabbit snare', which was simply an ordinary snare with a knot in the wire which prevented the noose tightening beyond a certain point. A main argument in its favour was that rabbits so taken could either be killed or liberated elsewhere if required, a suggestion which indicates that even by the close of the nineteenth century the policy towards the rabbit was not invariably one of extermination.

One disadvantage of setting snares in the open is the risk of passers-by, human or otherwise, benefiting from your skill. (Although in the old days keepers finding a poacher's snare would, far from taking a rabbit out, actually put one in to assist a successful prosecution.) If several snared rabbits are partly eaten the culprit is probably a fox, for a dog will finish one completely before moving to another. Both dog and fox will, when satisfied, try to carry away and bury either whole or partial carcasses. A cat partly eats the rabbit, leaving the remains in the snare.

Although the gin trap played such a major part in rabbit control, I have been unable to trace its date of origin. The truth is probably that it was known as an effective device for many years before improving manufacturing techniques and materials made its mass-production possible, and its introduction was by slow degrees. Harting, that most prolific source, reports the second edition of the *Book of St. Albans*, 1496, on the subject of the avocation of the fowler, 'many a gynne and many a snare he makyth', and from Shakespeare:

> 'Now is the woodcock near the gin'
>
> *Twelfth Night*, Act ii, sc. 5

and

> 'So strives the woodcock with the gin'
>
> *Henry VI*, Part 3, Act i, sc. 4

In 1653 Izaak Walton, in his *Compleat Angler*, wrote of 'the pleasure it is sometimes with gins to betray the very vermin of the earth'. Harting believes the name gin is of Scandanavian origin, as the Icelandic *ginna* means to dupe or deceive. An alternative derivation is a contraction of the French *engin*, meaning a contrivance or piece of ingenuity.

The principle of the gin was not restricted to the capture of rabbits, but in different sizes applied to such extremes as weasels, rats and men. (Plate 23 shows a photograph of a man-trap.) Essentially it consists of two rows of metal teeth which clamp together with great force when the victim treads on a thin metal plate and thereby activates a spring. Many earlier models were badly made in both workmanship and material, and unreliable. Any reader wanting to study gins in detail should read *Practical Trapping*, by W. Carnegie, which was published in 1880 and is a mine of information. Although original copies are now very scarce it was republished in a facsimile edition by Tideline Books in 1973 and is readily obtainable. *The Field* of 26 March 1887 described an improved gin known as Burgess's Spring Trap, but the big seller of the period appears to have been the model produced by F. Lane of Plymouth. Carnegie said of it, and in so doing pointed to the shortcomings of its rivals, 'Most gins are wholly made of iron, but in this it is not so, and zinc and copper are introduced. The spring, the most important part of the trap, is always thoroughly well tempered, is strong, but nevertheless easily pressed down when the trap is being set; the flap and catch and other important parts, in which most makers fail, are of copper, and do not wear away like iron, nor rust, which would clog the trap and prevent its acting.' Incidentally these superior traps were 'slightly dearer than the ordinary ones', costing 1s 9d each, 'but a reduction is made by the dozen'.

It was important that the teeth of the gin were neither sharp nor pointed and they were not required to meet. These apparent imperfections actually meant that the unfortunate beast would be gripped by the legs and held, for otherwise the legs might be severed and the rabbit escape. To prevent the rabbit dragging both itself and the gin away a short length of chain and a swivel were connected to a peg driven into the ground. Like the snare the gin was set in the run, at the point where the rabbit actually landed as it leapt along. A section of turf or soil was removed, the gin set and placed in the depression, concealed and the ground level restored by sprinkling loose soil over it.

In the West of England to set or place a gin was to 'till' it. Once set or tilled they could be left for four days, unless it rained when they would need resetting and recovering. Frost also necessitated resetting. Gins needed visiting at dawn and dusk, although Carnegie recommended a midnight visit if the moon was good. As an example of their effectiveness he claimed that on one night he set sixty traps and by the following morning had fifty-six rabbits.

The gin was a dreadfully cruel way of taking rabbits and many millions perished in this way before its abolition in 1958. In fact, restrictions were placed upon its use by the Ground Game Act of 1880, but these were not for the sake of the rabbit but for any game bird, fox or dog which might tread on a gin set in the open. Under the Act (43 & 44 Vict., c. 47) 'No person shall, for the purpose of killing ground game, employ spring traps except in rabbits' holes.' However, in 1885, in *Smith* v. *Hunt*, the Court of the Queen's Bench decided this section did not apply to owner occupiers. Many others did not bother to test the views of the Queen's Bench and simply carried on setting gins where they wished. It appears that within a few years this provision of the law was largely ignored. (Ryves in *Bird Life in Cornwall*, 1948, reports the cliffs of Cornwall as 'thickly sown with open gins'.) The ease with which relatively unskilled men could catch rabbits with gins was a factor in the disappearance of the large rabbit warrens, and as the demand for rabbits continued unabated the profession of rabbit trapper grew. Sheail reports a Pembrokeshire trapper employing forty trappers working in the sand dunes of the south Welsh coast before the first World War and catching as many as 3,000 rabbits in a night.

The obvious cruelty of the gin attracted much criticism and in 1911 The Protection of Animals' Act made it compulsory for every trapper to inspect his gins between sunrise and sunset. As with much other legislation it is easier to work out rules and regulations in the orderly setting of Parliament than to enforce it in the rude world outside, particularly the countryside where there are few observers of a man's actions. It is doubtful if this Act did much to alleviate the sufferings of the rabbit. A Select Committee of 1934, set up to look into the use of traps, disagreed with the proposition that the gin was the most cruel way of killing rabbits and cited various alternatives. The gin was, they believed, the only way of controlling the rabbit until a better substitute was found. Ironically by the time it was, nature had produced her own answer—myxomatosis.

The search for a more humane trap produced some weird and ingenious devices, of which one of the better was the Sawyer humane rabbit trap. Sedgwick in *Wildfowling and Rough Shooting* (1950) writes of his experiences with it, criticizing it on the grounds of slowness to set up and a 'very real sense of personal fear while setting each'. Eventually the Sawyer joined the long list of other also-rans and, as I write, the only traps which may legally be used for rabbits are the Imbra, the Juby and the Fenn Mark I (Rabbit). All work on the same principle as the gin, but in place of the jaws are two 'arms' operated by a strong spring. Once released they clap together around the neck or near the heart, usually killing the rabbit outright.

It would be interesting to know whether early men devised the snare or the net first. Possibly the net came first, for the most primitive attempt to capture something is to pursue it and, having cornered and then lost the quarry, it would be natural to think of some way of containing or restricting it. Whatever the answer the fact remains that nets have taken a great toll of rabbits over the years. The princely form of netting, alongside which all others are mere diversions, is the long-net, now little used but once in common use by both legal and illegal pursuers of the rabbit. The best long-nets were made of silk for lightness, and rarely shorter than fifty yards (45 m) or longer than a hundred (90 m). The width was usually five feet (1·5 m) and the meshes 2½ inches (6·3 cm) square, which size allowed young rabbits to squeeze through. What they cost I cannot say, but of course many would have been knitted by a cottage fireside. Obviously they were expensive, for Barkley's *Rat-Catching* says that a rabbit-catcher in full swing would need eight hundred to a thousand yards (732–914 m) and added, 'I fear it will be some time before the ordinary rabbit-catcher will be able to afford it.' My latest catalogue dated September 1976 lists green nylon long-nets, three feet high (0·9 m) and one hundred yards (91·4 m) long, for £24, which sum would have employed two farm workers for a full year only a century ago.

As with some other aspects covered by this book it is difficult to avoid the impression that many of the men who have written about long-netting have little practical experience and those who have could not or did not write. Payne-Gallwey in his *Letters to Young Shooters* wrote, 'When you use nets to catch rabbits, have them made with their lower halves of light cord, and their upper of dark (this does not add to the cost), the lower and lighter half will then appear to a rabbit as an opening under the darker part, and he will unhesitatingly run into it.' Harting demolishes this suggestion by pointing out that after a few wet nights of wet grass and tramplings underfoot the entire net would be of uniform colour.

Long-netting is practised at night and the art of the game is to set up the net, in complete silence, along the fringe of a covert and thereby cut off from their homes those resident rabbits which have moved out into the adjoining fields to feed. With the net erected the rabbits are driven towards home, caught in the net and killed—once again a simple description of a difficult exercise. It is not an operation I have ever performed, although I would like to, and there is certainly no lack of direction from various authorities. Unfortunately they are not in complete agreement. Harting says, 'A tolerably dark night should be selected with the wind blowing from the covert.' Perfectly clear—but then consider Ian Niall in *The New Poacher's Handbook* (1960), 'One of the secrets is in knowing where to set and another in setting so that the wind billows the net away from the running rabbit.'

Although Niall says one of the secrets is knowing where to set he offers no advice. Harting is kinder, suggesting about two yards from the side of the covert, and pointing out that men working close to the covert edge will be less visible to grazing rabbits than if further away. It is not a job you will accomplish alone for even the setting out requires two, one to work down the covert side driving in the wooden sticks or pegs some ten yards (*c.* 9·14 m) apart, while the other follows, uncoiling the net and attaching the top cord to the top of each stick. The process of driving the rabbits in can be carried out by a man alone or, if the area to be covered is large, a dog can be used (preferably one that is steady to fur or the resulting chaos as a terrified rabbit strikes the net, to be followed shortly after by a large dog going at top speed, can be imagined). Harting describes the use of a 'dead dog', which was a long line trailed across the field by a man at each end.

While Niall's book purported to advise poachers on their calling, Harting advised owners on how to frustrate them. The cure for long-netting, he suggested, was to have a keeper go round every night and run the rabbits in, at the same time seeing the surrounding fields were well 'brushed' to foul the nets. After a time the rabbits would learn to start feeding earlier and return home before the arrival of any poachers.

Barkley gives a rousing account of the novel practice of surrounding areas of rabbit-infested gorse with long-nets after previously stinking the rabbit burrows out. When all is set a pack of terriers is turned in to cries of 'Yap! yap! yap! Hie in, good dogs! hie in, young ones! Ah! back there! back! no going over the nets! Would you? Look here! hie there! in you go! Yap!

yap! yap!' One suspects Barkley's printer had to send out for a further supply of exclamation marks.

A miniature long-net called a gate or sheet-net was used for taking hares. Some six or seven yards long and six feet high, it was hung across a gate habitually used by hares and 'puss' driven to it.

Purse-nets will, of course, be dealt with in the chapter on ferreting, but Niall describes a novel form of using them. He once observed a gypsy working his whippet through a secluded hollow until the dog marked a rabbit in a blackberry bush. The gypsy then netted every exit, and tossed stones into the bush until the rabbit bolted and was caught.

Man's ingenuity in pursuit of the rabbit has extended to seeking the help of other creatures. Foremost among these is the lurcher, but its story must await the chapter on poaching. Less well known was the practice of rabbit-shooting in coverts with the use of beagles. They were not used where coverts were small or hares, a most distracting influence, numerous; but in large open coverts, particularly in Sussex, shooting to beagles was fairly common. Among their many virtues was listed the melodious music as they gave tongue, although if they rose a fox this happy sound would soon fade into the distance and sport would cease for some time.

While on the ground man sought help from dog and ferret; in the air it was the goshawk, and the chapter that deals with rabbit-hawking is one of the most interesting in Harting's book. The sport is a very old one and goshawks and rabbits were mentioned in the *Book of St. Albans* in 1486. It was also still very much alive at the beginning of this century for Harting gives detailed directions on how to procure a goshawk. No nest having been found in this country for some years, the secret was to send to France or Germany. From a dealer in the latter country a bird might be purchased for a couple of pounds or so, but the flight feathers might be imperfect and it was thought better to pay a little more for a good one from, for example, the Jardin d'Acclimatation in Paris. 'Hints on the Management of Hawks' was the recommended manual, and obtainable from *The Field* office. Various suggestions on training followed, eventually culminating in the great moment when the hawk was ready to be 'entered' at a live rabbit. A young rabbit had to be taken alive, by ferreting, and placed under an inverted flower-pot with a piece of string attached to the top. With the goshawk in position the string would be pulled, the rabbit would bolt and, with luck, the goshawk would swoop.

The ability of a trained adult goshawk to take rabbits was obviously considerable. Harting reports that a goshawk belonging to Mr. John Riley of Putley Court, Herefordshire, took 70 rabbits in fifteen days. And in *The Field* of 2 May 1896, Sir Harry Boynton of Burton Agnes, Hull, wrote, 'It may interest some of your readers, who are lovers of falconry, to learn what I have done with a nestling goshawk which I brought from Nordland, Norway in June 1895. She killed her first wild rabbit on 17th September. Her two best days were as follows: the best, 24 rabbits out of 24 flights; the next best day, 20 rabbits out of 24 flights. The hawk had, throughout the season, on an average, a three-quarter crop a day, and was consequently in the very highest condition, which rendered her able to undergo the hardiest work that a hawk is capable of enduring. She was flown on seventy days, and the total bag for the season was: rabbits 407, hare 1, rats, 5, stoat 1, weasel 1, total 415 head; and every one of the quarry mentioned was killed in fair flight, without being handled in any way.'

It is interesting to contrast this obvious ability of the goshawk with my conclusions on the ability of the buzzard as a rabbit killer, given in chapter 3.

Returning once again to man's efforts it is interesting to note how the techniques of rabbit catching varied with the density of the rabbits and their surroundings, achieving almost mass-production standards in the thickly populated warrens. The tip-trap, also known as a tipe or type earlier, was in common use. Sheail described them as circular pits, eight to nine feet (2·4 m to 2·7 m) deep, and lined with wood, chalk, flint or birch, but Harting writes of 'a kind of cistern'. The cavity was covered with a door or lid, balanced on a hinge pin through the centre which would give way and drop any rabbit that crossed it into the pit. The pit-traps were permanent installations, sited along much-used runs and with the lid normally bolted. When the bolt was withdrawn the catch could be prodigious, and Harting writes of it being possible to take five or six hundred rabbits in a night. Pit-traps had to be visited frequently during the night, principally to remove the rabbits to prevent them being crushed and spoilt by the weight of those still to come, but also to prevent poachers seizing an opportunity for a large and easy haul.

No consideration of methods of taking rabbits would be complete without examining the various forms of shooting. In most forms the rabbit is shot whilst bolting for or through cover, but rabbits as well as the mighty deer can be stalked, and great sport it is too. On a summer evening, as twilight gathers, rabbits will emerge from cover and sit quietly waiting for the light to go before they move away from safety to feed. To stalk them on a still night, when a cracking twig or chinking stone will send them scuttering below, calls for care and patience. Although the job can be done with a shotgun it is a clumsy weapon for an otherwise delicate operation and a ·22 rifle is more satisfying. It has the further advantage that, used with a low velocity bullet, the noise is far less and one shot will not end your sport for an hour or so as with a shotgun. Payne-Gallwey gives an excellent description of rabbit stalking with a 'pea rifle' in the Badminton Library's *Shooting: Field and Covert*, mentioning that 'During the summer months hundreds of rabbits may be seen sitting out in the meadows surrounding every covert and in thousands in many a park.' It is not an easy sport, for even when you have managed to approach within range, a rabbit in the lush grass of summer at a range of fifty yards or so is not an easy target.

Night shooting from vehicles is effective and sport of a sort. The best vehicle is a small open pick-up or open Land Rover, from the back of which the shooter can support himself on the cab roof, while shooting forward at rabbits picked up in the headlights. A few bales of straw carefully wedged in the back give solid supports to brace the feet and knees against. The technique is to drive along the hedgerows at night, selecting, of course, those fields where no crop can be damaged, shooting the rabbits as they dash back for cover. The commotion of shots, lights and engine noise puts the majority down before you are within range but large bags are possible. It does not, I confess, appeal to me, for the poor creatures are often confused and to pursue them with such artificial aids is wrong. By all means do it if you want to eliminate rabbits, but if sport is the purpose then the ideal aids are a gun and a spaniel.

There is another more practical objection to night shooting

rabbits from a vehicle, which is that, except in certain circumstances, the practice is illegal. The fact is not generally known, but Section 6 of the Ground Game (Amendment) Act 1906 prohibits the exercise of the right to kill ground game by the use of firearms at night. The only exception appears to be a landowner in occupation with his sporting rights in hand or the grantee of the rights from such an owner. In all other cases, including an occupier (which description will include a tenant) holding the sporting rights over his land by virtue of the fact of his occupation (*Saunders* v. *Pitfield*, 1888 and *Waters* v. *Phillips*, 1910), the prohibition applies. Nor can an occupier, as distinct from an owner in occupation, grant the right to shoot ground game at night to anyone. There must be many shooting men who have unwittingly broken the law by night shooting rabbits.

Harvest field shooting is a very different matter to night shooting—this really is sport! In fact the golden days are over now, for rabbits are fewer, combines leave too high a stubble and the pace of modern agriculture leaves no time for frivolities. But those readers who enjoyed the real thing will need little reminding. I call easily to mind the cornfields of Norfolk in the days before the last war. Mile after waving mile of small cornfields, bottles of lemonade lying in the cool of the ditch marking the presence of a work-force, and the binder clanking round the perimeter of the corn, drawn by two large powerful horses, which not many months previously had pulled the steel of the plough through the same field. As the little patch of standing corn in the centre shrank so the rabbits would begin to bolt; at first just the occasional adventurer, but ever-more frequently until with only a narrow strip standing they would break in all directions and chaos reigned. Farmers and their men, some with guns and others with sticks, would be firing or chasing, while a motley collection of badly trained spaniels, labradors and lurchers would have their own private coursing matches. Perhaps, somewhere, a harvest field shoot was conducted with order and discipline, but if so I never saw it. The truth may be that no one wanted it any other way for harvest, without modern machines, was a time of intensive hard work that dragged on for weeks. The brief periods of sport were doubtless as much a psychological safety valve as a means of killing rabbits.

If you have enough rabbits to justify a serious harvest field shoot, there are a few points worth remembering. If you 'stink-out' the adjoining burrows beforehand there will be many more in the corn when you cut. Rabbits will not leave the corn haphazardly unless hard pressed, but will run for known good cover. These routes should be watched and if there are not enough Guns to surround the corn put a scarecrow on the opposite side. If the field cannot be finished in the day it is pointless to shoot it the next for the rabbits will leave the corn overnight.

For me, and doubtless for you too, the best sport with rabbits comes with rough shooting them from cover. Ferreting is fun, but the delays can be trying, and on a cold day hanging about can become a miserable business. Even on the coldest day there is enough movement in rough shooting to keep warm and, most important, it contains the pleasure of working your dog or dogs. Beats there the heart which does not quicken at the sight of a spaniel working rabbits? With legs of sprung steel, tail-a-quiver, ears cocked—if I had to be born again and as an animal, it would be as a springer to a rough shooter.

It is exciting shooting, calling for a quick but disciplined eye and brain. Too slow, and the flash of brown with a white scut is across the ride and gone; too quick, and you can be dangerous. Never try to take a rabbit off the nose of a dog. Where rabbits are present almost any cover may hold one, but often the problem is to compel it to break cover for long enough to present a chance. I shoot a wood with a carpet of large patches of bramble and often we may work a rabbit for some distance and never see it.

In spite of their other virtues labradors are inferior to spaniels for rabbit shooting, being too large and lacking the spaniel's willingness to hurl itself into a pin cushion of bramble thorns at the merest hint that a rabbit might be within. Terriers were, and indeed still are in some places, frequently used for rabbit shooting, but Payne-Gallwey, in *Shooting*, goes to great lengths to advise against them. They are, he says, far too excitable and range too far, and being of a hound species, will follow a line as far as they can, and 'worst of all, when they can mark the rabbit to ground they cannot resist the temptation of following him there and working away under the surface perhaps for half an hour, just when their aid is most needed above ground, to emerge with coat and eyes full of sand, half-suffocated, and more tired and exhausted than if they had roused a dozen rabbits from the covert to afford nice shots for their master'. Harting also expresses a preference for spaniels over terriers, mainly because of their ability to retrieve. Incidentally, for sheer excitement it would be hard to beat Harting's description in *The Rabbit* of a day's rabbit shooting on a furze common. Where the ground is bare Harting suggests making rabbit cover by scattering branches of thorns about the fields in spring. Grain will grow through these and the thorns will stop cattle eating it.

The best rough shooting can only be obtained by 'stinking-out' the burrows, but we will return to this art later and for the moment consider large-scale team shooting for rabbits by driving coverts. Like so many other forms of rabbit pursuit formal covert shooting has fallen into disuse since myxomatosis. However, local population explosions make it a worthwhile activity and justify a detailed description.

Quite illogically rabbit drives are often considered an excellent opportunity for the young or inexperienced shot. Nothing could be more untrue, for these are potentially some of the most dangerous occasions in shooting and only well tried Guns should be allowed. With a line of beaters walking towards a line of Guns, rabbits bolting in all directions, guns being fired anywhere but in the air, and a mass of trees and ground growth to ricochet shot, the situation is alive with risks. Basically the Guns line a ride while the beaters drive a stretch of woodland towards them. Some shoots allow Guns to walk with the beaters, but the safest course is to have few, if any, and these on the flanks to pick up any rabbits bursting sideways. The standing Guns must not, of course, fire forwards, and if the ground cover is thick they may only be able to fire along the ride. With fellow Guns on either side, the ride will need to be fairly wide, and the Guns to be keeping in a strict line, if this is to be possible. Perhaps the best scheme is for the standing Guns to stand with their backs to the beaters, and tight onto the edge from which the rabbits will bolt. Any shot will then be taken away from the beating line and the maximum time is given for a shot. Most of the shots will be close and a lightly loaded cartridge, with a small shot size, will, if properly directed, do the job perfectly well and damage the rabbit less than a standard load. (Interestingly, Teasdale-Buckell in *The Complete Shot* recommended cartridges loaded with $\frac{3}{4}$ oz. of no. 3 shot!) It goes almost without saying that an open-choked gun is desirable, and even then the comment of a distinguished statesman, that the only fault of a rabbit is that it is six inches too short, holds good.

In the last century rabbit 'battues' in the coverts were taken very seriously, both by the keepers and the Guns, with preparation beginning several days in advance. 'Stinking-out' was the main essential for a big bag, followed by a steady line of beaters prepared to tackle any cover, no matter how thick or thorny. On these formal occasions dogs were usually excluded. Sometimes the ground to be shot would be wild park-land, covered with dead bracken, and rides would be cut through this. Payne-Gallwey writes of bags up to five thousand in a day by this method. Harting, on the subject of rabbit shooting in coverts, regarded the placing of stops and pegging long-nets along the flank rides as preliminaries which could 'be taken for granted'.

Moving into more modern times, there are some excellent accounts of covert shooting rabbits in Tommy Turner's *Memoirs of a Gamekeeper* (1954). Of one drive he wrote, 'By then rabbits were running about in hundreds, at least it seemed like it, and the beaters went completely mad, as they will do sometimes with rabbits, hollering and yelling, hitting at the rabbits, knocking some of the uprooted trees down, often on each other. You have never heard such a noise. By then the smoke from the shooting which hung in the damp atmosphere had become almost a thick fog, some of the Guns had unloaded and were swinging their gun barrels about trying to cool them down. I nearly blew my lungs down my horn trying to halt the line for a bit, which I eventually succeeded in doing, but the rabbits kept coming on just the same, so I let them carry on.'

On this occasion just over 400 rabbits were killed by five Guns in forty minutes. Perhaps more remarkable was a day in 1948 which was entirely concentrated on 25 acres (*c.* 10 h) of kale, through which rides had been cut, and which yielded a bag of no less than 778 rabbits. Also in 1948, Turner reports a field of kale which was shot on three separate occasions, producing a total of nearly 1,200 rabbits. Turner was, as befits a headkeeper, meticulous in preserving accurate bag records, and his book is scattered with rabbit bags of several hundred in a day, and on at least three occasions more than 300 in a single drive. Turner observed over the years that rabbits always drove better downwind than upwind and put this down to their dislike of the smell of burnt powder drifting downwind after the first few shots had been fired. Although his book is written in the formal terms of a man who grew up 'knowing his place', the occasional shaft of humour strikes through, and when driving rabbits he always explained to the Guns that they must be placed downwind as the rabbits were less offended by the smell of the beaters.

Turner's estate gave considerable thought to the matter of safety at rabbit drives and eventually evolved a simple but very effective technique. All the Guns would stand on the edge of the covert being beaten and with their backs to it. They would then all turn half-right (it could as easily be half-left) and only shoot rabbits within this angle. In this way they always fired away from the beaters, had the maximum time to shoot, avoided the need to be watching through 180 degrees and, most important, if a pellet ricocheted it could never hit another Gun in the face for any individual Gun could only see the backs of those in the direction he was firing.

Another device, produced to overcome the problem of men's scent turning back rabbits, but none the less a contribution to safety, was to build platforms several feet off the ground.

At last we reach the interesting business of 'stinking out' rabbits. The theory is very simple. Rabbits, when you want to shoot them, are frequently uncooperative and skulking in their burrows. The first solution is to drive them out with ferrets. The second, a logical progression from the first, is to discourage them from going below ground in the first place, and this is done by pushing into the holes some foul smelling substance the day before you shoot. A single hole in each burrow should be untreated, to permit the inhabitants' departure, and if special attention is given to the upwind holes, the smell should spread throughout the burrow.

The practice is straightforward; the interest comes from the various concoctions devised over the years for producing the smell. Paraffin is a firm favourite, either soaked in paper or fir cones, or placed in containers of empty cartridge cases. Some want it well down the hole and others are content to rub it around the entrance with rags tied on a stick. Even more original is the practice of running ferrets through with their backs painted with paraffin. (Renardine is an alternative.)

Harting advocated a very thorough programme spread over six days. On the first every hole was stopped. On the second some were opened, an eight-inch (20 cm) peg with a slit in the top was stuck into the ground immediately beside each, and paper soaked in paraffin was inserted into the slit. On the third day all the open holes were closed again. The fourth day the papers were resoaked in paraffin, and on the fifth any reopened holes were stopped. The sixth day the covert was shot.

This programme closely follows the advice given by Payne-Gallwey in *Shooting*, who points out that it has the great advantage of leaving the burrows unpolluted and those rabbits which survive the shoot will rapidly open up the stopped holes and resume normal living. Payne-Gallwey recommended spirits of tar as superior to paraffin. Barkley agreed, but smeared his over a muzzled and lined ferret and ran it a little way down each hole, returning the next day to stop the holes. On each stopping sod he pegged a piece of paper to stop the rabbits digging it out.

Perhaps such detail is not necessary, for Payne-Gallwey, having given instructions for a most laborious exercise, in another part of *Shooting* says, 'If a ferret, muzzled, be run through all the holes about two days beforehand, most of the rabbits will be found sitting out.'

Sheail gives two recipes for stinking out. The first is a rag, dipped into sulphur paste, tied onto a stick, set on fire and pushed down a hole for a minute or so. The other deserves to succeed, if only because its preparation must have been an ordeal. Take 1½ lb. (42·5 g) soft soap, 2 lb. (56·7 g) black sulphur, ½ gallon (2·27 l) tar, 1 quart (1·14 l) spirit of tar, ½ gallon (2·27 l) of paraffin, 1 quart (1·14 l) train oil; mix them and then boil slowly.

After this it is a relief to learn there are other cleaner ways of keeping rabbits above ground. Payne-Gallwey recommended sending keepers with lanterns and dogs to patrol the feeding ground for several nights before the shooting, so compelling the rabbits to feed and lie-out during the day. But perhaps the weary keepers would have preferred mixing black sulphur and train oil during the day and sleeping at night.

It is far harder to keep rabbits above ground in wet weather, when a previously unacceptable smell becomes preferable to lying in wet cover, and Payne-Gallwey devised a plan to overcome this. He was, incidentally, a most ingenious man, constantly turning an agile mind to all manner of shooting problems. For example, when working on his theories over shooting high pheasants he strapped some newly killed birds to a frame, flew it forty yards above the ground from a kite and fired at the carcasses to investigate pellet penetration. However, I suspect not all his ideas were practical, as witness his 'wet weather' scheme, published in his *Letters to Young Shooters*. The plan required surrounding the burrow or even, he suggested, a small wood, with a three-foot-high (0·9 m) wire netting fence with the wire bent outwards for for the bottom six inches (15·2 cm) and pegged down. Boards had then to be leaned on the inside, from the ground to the top of the wire fence and covered with sods. Once the fence was built the rabbits would emerge for their nightly feed and find themselves cut off from their feeding grounds. After a day or so hunger would force them to explore, when they would use the bridges, jump down from the top of the fence and be unable to return.

Perhaps it worked in 1894 but in 1976 the cost of wire and labour makes it unthinkable.

Now the wheel has swung full circle and to kill rabbits we aim at getting them underground to gas them rather than above ground to shoot them. The loss of the carcasses is unfortunate but labour is now so expensive and rabbits so relatively few that it is not economic sense to practise techniques aimed at producing saleable carcasses. The procedure is to shoot any outlying rabbits or, in the process, drive them underground, where they are gassed with hydrocyanic gas. The technique is simple and effective. A spoonful of a proprietary powdered cyanide compound, such as Cymag, is placed about six inches (15·2 cm) down a hole, and the hole sealed with a sod. Every hole in a burrow must be treated and the powder, on making contact with the moisture in the atmosphere, gives off the hydrocyanic gas. With a larger burrow the powder needs to be blown through with a pump and the size of the burrow or warren will determine whether a hand or power pump is needed.

Full details of gassing are given in the Game Conservancy booklet No. 22 *Rabbit Control*, but for those who do not read it I would mention that they stress that gassing, of any form, should never be carried out alone as the gas can rapidly cause loss of consciousness. Some simple rules are never to stand downwind; not to take a dog; always wash thoroughly afterwards; bury empty tins; do not gas in windy or wet weather; and do not wash your equipment in lakes, ponds, rivers or streams. The Ministry of Agriculture's pamphlet *Safe Handling—Cyanide Gassing Powders* should also be read.

Rabbits must, of course, be controlled but gassing is an unpleasant way to kill anything and I will not dwell on it.

CHAPTER EIGHT

Ferreting

Those who know nothing of the details of ferreting will consider it a very simple exercise—a ferret is popped into a burrow and drives out the inhabitants. Those who have followed the sport know better.

The first question is whether or not ferrets need training and, if so, how. William Thomas, whose excellent *Rabbit Shooting to Ferrets* (1946) entitles his opinion to respect, says that no training is necessary as all work below ground is purely instinctive. He does, however, place great stress on teaching young ferrets to come to call, arguing that if the training is well done they can later be readily called from a burrow. He begins when the kittens are only eight to ten weeks old by placing them a few feet downwind of their mother. They can both see and smell her and, as they make for her, he calls them, handling them as they arrive. This exercise is repeated twice a day, gradually increasing the distance and facing the kittens in the opposite direction so they have to rely on hearing. The bait that brings them is their mother, but after a few weeks she is superseded by food and the calling done at meal times. In general he advocates handling and playing with young ferrets as one would puppies.

The reasons are both obvious and laudable but his training has nothing to do with teaching a ferret to bolt rabbits. Niblett has more positive views on training. He advocates taking the mother and two of her offspring to a small burrow where there is almost certainly a rabbit or two in occupation. The mother should be allowed to go in a short distance on a line and the youngsters encouraged to follow. Once they do the line is cast off and they will then either bolt a rabbit or kill below—either way they will have learnt something. Next he suggests working the two youngsters, without the mother, in small burrows where you do not expect to find rabbits but where some scent may be expected. Here they will learn to explore underground and lose their initial fears of the unknown. Niblett believes in netting rabbits, not shooting, whilst training. In this way a bolting rabbit could be killed at once and left in position for the young ferret to find and worry when it emerged.

As a side issue, many people believe that using a ferret for ratting ruins it for rabbiting as it makes it fierce. Samuel and Lloyd disagree, arguing that ferrets are fierce anyway, and that properly and regularly handled, once tamed they stay tamed whatever quarry they pursue. Others have a contrary experience and I would personally not use my ferrets for rats, if only because of the risk of their being severely wounded.

Some early writers advocated training a ferret by releasing it into a pipe or series of pipes, culminating in one with a captive rabbit. No doubt the technique worked but it was both cruel and unnecessary.

Ferret training is simply a matter of commonsense. The first essential is to tame the ferret and, apart from the odd rogue, this is just a question of frequent quiet handling. Ferrets are affectionate and playful. They quickly grow to enjoy being handled and with our ferrets there is no need to pick them up—if an arm is thrust into the run every ferret in sight scampers up it. Apart from the sheer pleasure of contact with such pleasant animals, gaining their confidence and affection pays dividends later. A tame ferret will emerge readily from a rabbit hole, whereas one which is handled rarely, and then with thick gloves, peers suspiciously out then backs down, chattering with fear, when approached.

Teaching them to come to call or whistle as Thomas recommends, is useful, although not always as effective as it sounds in theory. Personally I have no use for pipes or other artificial devices. Find a small burrow of not more than half a dozen holes and with no digging problems and run an adult ferret through to make sure it is empty. Take the youngster, chat to it for a moment or two and place it in a hole entrance. Do *not* force it in or prevent it backing out. In all probability it will investigate for a yard or so, become worried when the light fades and return. Fondle it, place it in another hole, let it explore and generally let it progress at its own pace. If the youngster is reluctant then introduce the mother to set an example. It is very rare to encounter any difficulty—the main problem lies not with the ferret but with you. You must curtail your enthusiasm to push the ferret on too quickly. It is just a child and should not be worked in large or difficult burrows until it is experienced and confident in smaller ones.

There is no need at all to teach ferrets to hunt rabbits; indeed, it would be a remarkable man who taught one not to. Nor can you teach a ferret to bolt rabbits, for contrary to what some writers have suggested, I do not believe any ferret ever consciously set out to bolt rabbits. Ferrets pursue rabbits with the object of killing them and the rabbit bolts to escape. For this reason large, strong ferrets are not always the best bolters for they often catch, kill and lay-up. Rabbits can more easily escape and bolt from smaller weaker ferrets.

One would not normally go ferreting with less than two ferrets and one of these should be an experienced adult.

I described various ways of carrying ferrets in Chapter 6, personally advocating a box for the greater safety of the ferret. Nets are dealt with later in this chapter, but if you are using this method you will need a plentiful supply. If not there is the gun and cartridges, preferably with a sleeve, for it is very easy to dent a stock or barrel when carrying a gun with all the other paraphernalia of ferreting. A suitable spade or 'graft' is essential as are all the other items required to resolve a lay-up. This aspect of ferreting is so important that I cover it in detail in the following chapter. There are other useful oddments, one of the most being a stout glove to wear when thrusting an arm down a hole to explore a rumpus heard close by. Even the tamest of ferrets battling with a rabbit in the dark cannot be expected to distinguish a friendly hand and rabbits can also inflict a deep bite. If a long day is envisaged take some milk for the ferrets for they grow very thirsty.

Which leads us neatly to the question of whether or not to feed the ferrets on the day they are due to work. Here indeed the authorities are at variance. There are two schools of thought—one says ferrets should be starved before working so they go about their job keenly. The other reasons that a ferret should be normally fed or it will kill and lay-up to eat at the first opportunity. Barkley was an exponent of the starving theory, feeding his ferrets on the morning of the day *before* they worked and nothing more until they had finished. Thomas was less severe, giving a light drink in the morning and cutting the previous evening's meal to two thirds of normal. Everitt was a stage nearer normal feeding, cutting out only the morning feed on the day but giving milk a couple of hours or so before work began. Niblett and also Samuel and Lloyd all advocate normal feeding and, to me, this seems far and away the best course. No ferret I have ever seen needed starving to make it keen—their whole existence has been centred on pursuing rabbits. Conversely, if you send a hungry ferret after rabbits a lay-up seems inevitable. In particular, Barkley's advice would mean the ferrets would not have fed for nearly thirty-six hours and while I accept they would have been keen, a lay-up would have been protracted. It should not be inferred from Barkley's advice that he was unconcerned with the welfare of his ferrets; it would be wrong to leave this subject without quoting a gem from his *Studies in the Art of Rat-Catching*, 'When I have done work and turned towards home, I have made it a rule always to put a dead rat into the bag, as I think it amuses the ferrets and breaks the monotony of a long journey; just as when I run down home I like taking a snack at Swindon Station, just to divert my mind from the racketing of the train and the thought of the hard seat.'

With ferrets trained and fed (or not fed, if such is your inclination), we are ready to begin. But when and where? One answer, obvious to the old hand but not to the novice, is not when there are young rabbits about, for these are easily caught by the ferrets and constant lay-ups will ensue. (Additionally, although this should only be whispered if there are farmers nearby, you are killing off next winter's stock.) As breeding starts in earnest in March, February should be the last month for ferreting, although Harting recommends a cessation on 1 February. This would be impractical for those grounds where the coverts are sacrosanct until pheasant shooting ceases on that day.

'When' in the context of weather conditions is something over which experts disagree, although many argue over detail rather than basic principles. Payne-Gallwey was most at variance with other authors, declaring that 'it requires a windy day for rabbits to bolt well; they bolt better before midday than after.' Perhaps he was not a close observer of the sport of ferreting, for he wrote, 'Ferreting is the least exciting form of rabbit shooting.' No other author shared Payne-Gallwey's view with the exception of Owen Jones in his *Sport of Shooting* (1928), who liked enough wind to carry off the above-ground noise (of which there should not, of course, be any). A brief summary of each expert's views is interesting. Payne-Gallwey's have been given; Owen Jones, in addition to his 'little wind', said they bolted best after a wet night but offered no reason why. This ties in with the views of Eric Parker in his *Elements of Shooting* (1924), who believed rabbits bolted badly after a good night's feeding, when full and sleepy, but well after a bad night (for example, wet), when hungry and restless. Parker also said results were worse on days of high, cold winds. Thomas agrees that cold winds are bad, but specifies they must be north-easterlies. Why, I cannot think, as I imagine a cold wind would have the same effect whether from north or east. On such days, he says, you should ferret deep in a wood and even then concentrate on those burrows in the lee of the wind. With cold winds Thomas also couples wet weather. Richard Jefferies agrees, saying, 'The rabbit is not easily dislodged in rain, for this animal avoids getting wet as much as possible; he "bolts" best when it is dry and still.' Carnegie went further and wrote that when it rains it is hard to get a rabbit to bolt at all.

Others inferred the problems of wind and rain by praising the reverse conditions for ferreting. Noel Sedgwick who, I suspect, had bolted very many more rabbits than Ralph Payne-Gallwey, recommended calm and frosty mornings and condemned wet and cold winds. Samuel and Lloyd said the best days were fine, crisp and frosty, and Tennyson in *Rough Shooting* (1938) agreed, adding that clammy mornings are worst. Niblett, on the same theme, wrote, 'The warm, muggy, summer-like day is unfortunately as bad for ferreting as it is for pike fishing.' He favoured settled weather and ideally in a frost or after a fall of snow when it had started to freeze again. Fred Taylor, in an excellent series of articles in the *Shooting Times* in the autumn of 1976, favoured frosty conditions but was least hopeful of success in snow, high winds or heavy rain. (Who wants to ferret in snow, high winds or heavy rain!)

In general, nearly all are agreed that rabbits bolt well in still, cold conditions, but are reluctant to bolt in rain or high winds. It is worth remembering that in a heavy frost digging out a laid-up ferret will be very hard work.

With the question of when to ferret settled, we can now turn to the less controversial matter of where. From the preceding paragraphs it is obvious, albeit surprising, that whether or not a rabbit flees before a ferret depends upon whether it likes the weather conditions above ground. Therefore in bad weather it is wise to work the most protected burrows, and this decision not only increases the chance of success but makes your own circumstances less uncomfortable in the event of a lay-up. Obviously time is saved, particularly when netting, if unoccupied burrows are avoided. In extreme cases the signs are clear enough. Abandoned burrows will have cobwebs, leaves and other debris in the hole entrances; there will be no fresh droppings in the vicinity and the runs will be overgrown. Do not, however, abandon such a burrow without checking all the holes for one or two rabbits may have reoccupied a section of it. The evidence of a well-occupied burrow is clear for all to read, with well-worn runs and holes and all the local vegetation well-cropped. In between these two extremes may be encountered many puzzles with enough evidence to suggest either partial or spasmodic occupation, but not enough to be sure. One tip is that flies are only seen in occupied burrows, but this of no help in the depths of winter. Harting recommended a terrier which would tell if a rabbit was at home, and Carnegie went further, claiming that a good dog would not only indicate occupation but point at the hole nearest to the rabbit. A dog which will do this, *and quietly*, is indeed a treasure, for it will help with lay-ups as well. The only way to be sure of a doubtful burrow is to run a ferret through it and if there are many such burrows then shooting is a far quicker method than netting.

In addition to knowing where to ferret it is wise to know where not to operate. Harting makes the point that rabbits much ferreted learn not to bolt and it is certainly true that if you work a good burrow frequently lay-ups become more common. There are also burrows worth avoiding because digging is impossible. Those formed in the roots of a large old tree are a good example and I personally knew several excellent burrows among the tumbled stones of Derbyshire hillsides which had to be avoided. Needless to say, these peaceful quarters prospered enormously. Another potentially difficult spot was under a timber chicken house, but although this yielded many rabbits I never had to take a saw to its floor. At first thought sand appears an easy form of soil to work. Unfortunately the rabbits agree and the burrows are usually both deep and extensive and what one gains in ease of digging is soon lost in the quantity to be moved. An additional problem is the danger of the collapsing sand suffocating the ferret and it is necessary to proceed with caution. Even without lay-ups there are problems, for the complexity of the burrows makes bolting difficult and the burrows are nearly always sited in marram grass, or other thick cover, and visibility is poor. In fact, some marram grass is so tunnelled as almost to provide an on-the-surface burrow. All in all, ferreting in sand is far from the easy task it first appears. (A sentence in which you may detect the sting of bitter experience!)

We move now to one of the most hotly disputed questions in the whole art—to muzzle or not to muzzle. The principle is simple enough—if you so restrict the movement of a ferret's mouth that it cannot bite, then it cannot kill and should not lay-up. Whether ferrets are muzzled or coped is merely a technical difference I will deal with shortly; the crux of the matter is whether they should be allowed free biting or not, and I will let the advocates of both sides plead their own cases. Consider Mr. Everitt, 'Working ferrets to rabbits, and training them to that branch of sport, for which they are most in request, is next to an impossibility unless muzzling and coping are thoroughly understood, both theoretically and practically,' or Mr. Barkley, 'It would have been madness to work the ferrets without muzzling them, for they would have been sure to kill some rabbits in the holes and then have laid up.' (In general, practically every mention of ferreting in older books is accompanied by instructions and diagrams on muzzling and coping.) For the defence we will hear that leading advocate Mr. Arthur Niblett, 'There are three ways of working ferrets when rabbiting: with a line, muzzled, or without a line or muzzle. The first named is both ineffectual and unpractical; the second should be had recourse to only when necessary; and the last is the way in which everyone who uses ferrets should endeavour to employ them.' Thomas is even more positive, 'I do not, in any circumstances, agree with or practise muzzling or coping.'

As the advocates of jaw confinement have a good argument why are Niblett and Thomas so against it? There are a variety of reasons. Niblett's objection to muzzling, which is done with a metal or leather device, is the excellent one that if the ferret is lost then it will inevitably starve to death. For this reason he argues that if you must prevent a ferret biting, then coping (which is simply using a muzzle made of string) is the better course, for the ferret will rid itself of this within a day or so. A subsidiary objection is that the weight of a muzzle tires a ferret sooner, but Niblett concludes with the critical argument that any form of jaw confinement increases rather than decreases delays through lay-ups. An unmuzzled ferret, he suggests, will kill quickly and, if a good one, leave the carcass quickly. A muzzled ferret will scratch and worry a cornered rabbit for a long time before it eventually gives up.

Thomas repeats Niblett's principal arguments and adds two more. Firstly, a muzzled ferret which spends a long time scratching at a rabbit it cannot kill not only wastes time but emerges very tired. Secondly, he is concerned for the safety of the ferret, saying, 'To send a ferret to ground muzzled or coped is like sending a soldier into battle handcuffed.' He points out that a ferret can easily encounter a rat, cat or even a little owl and, being courageous, will attack even though muzzled and probably be killed.

Thomas and Niblett have two points in common that are significant—they both show concern for the welfare of their ferrets and they have written two of the best books ever produced on ferreting. Once again the principle emerges that animals work best for those who have a genuine regard for them.

If you decide in favour of some form of muzzling or coping there are a variety of devices to choose from. An extremely effective and simple form of muzzle is a small brass ring which is slipped over the snout of the ferret, holding its mouth shut. A rod with a screw thread is then passed through a hole in the ring, behind the canine teeth, and is then screwed into a hole on the opposite side of the ring. There are variations on this, including a form which snaps into position by pressure, but all suffer the drawback that they are too effective and a lost ferret starves.

Leather muzzles are common, and consist of a ring around the snout with two thongs running back to a collar and buckle around the neck. Here again the ferret will be dead long before the leather rots, whereas with coping Niblett is emphatic that, properly done, the ferret will have freed itself in, at most, forty-eight hours. The procedure would be relatively simple were it not performed on a struggling ferret but no doubt you will improve with practice. Take a piece of soft string some twelve inches long, make a loop in the centre and, with a companion holding the ferret, lasso the bottom jaw of the ferret in the loop with the knot under the jaw. The string must be behind the first canine teeth and under the tongue. (The advantage of taming one's ferrets becomes apparent at this stage.) Pull the loop reasonably tight, knot once more and pass the two ends around the top jaw, knotting them above the nose. The two jaws are now held together by a form of figure of eight. Run the two pieces of string back along the head of the ferret and knot them together at the back of the skull. Finally loop the ends around the neck and knot them, although not too tightly. Niblett claimed often to have lost ferrets with this form of coping on but that they always turned up in good health and with the nose-piece worn through.

Niblett, you will recall, was against any form of muzzling and passed quickly over the subject, but Everitt, who regarded something of the sort as essential, devoted a whole chapter to detailing various devices and their good and bad points. To do him justice he had no time for muzzles, although his preference for coping was based not on the welfare of the ferret but on a belief that it worked better. The various monstrosities ferrets were expected to wear made this understandable, particularly the form of wire cage which enclosed the major part of the head. He devoted no less than eight pages to details of various forms of copes, most of which need not be repeated here. One point is, however, of considerable interest. Old time ferreters sometimes overcame the problem of muzzling by the simple but barbaric practice of sewing the lips of the ferret together with needle and thread. Niblett recalls the practice when ferreting with the keepers as a schoolboy on holiday and Niall mentions seeing it done by 'a cruel man'. Other writers mention and condemn it. but Everitt defended it. 'It may at first appear cruel,' he wrote, 'but after the first time or two there is no cruelty whatever, as the pierced holes remain permanently open as in a lady's ears.'

Creatures generally received less consideration in Everitt's day and some cruel practices existed to discourage ferrets from laying-up. One was to dab their feet with turpentine to irritate them and another was to tie a piece of string tightly around the tail. In both cases the sheer discomfort kept them from settling.

As the preceding paragraphs show there are various arguments for and against muzzling or coping and the newcomer to the sport must make up his own mind. In fact, the choice should really be between leaving the ferret unencumbered and coping as, for the reasons given, muzzling has no advantages over coping and several disadvantages. Personally, I work my ferrets free and very rarely have a long lay-up. The decision is partly humane, for gagging a creature which relies on its teeth for attack and defence must cause it some distress.

In spite of much handling some ferrets are still wary about being picked up. Niblett suggested a collar with a bootlace attached, to provide a form of lead. I see the utility of it but fear the lace might get caught up underground. An easier system is to dangle a dead rabbit before the ferret, which will always take a firm hold. This brings us to the matter of persuading a ferret to release a rabbit. Everitt recommended holding the rabbit in one hand and the ferret by the neck in the other. The thumb is then brought around the forehead and gradual pressure exerted at a point just over the eyes. Everitt claimed the ferret would let go instantly, but did not explain why this should be. Thomas had a more understandable method—he simply held the ferret with his forefinger under its neck and the weight of the rabbit pulled its head down. When he then pressed on the back of the ferret's neck with his thumb it had to let go to breathe. Always remember that a ferret which has just had contact with a rabbit will be excited and liable to bite.

Several points remain to tidy up the matter of ferrets. It is useless to expect a single ferret to bolt rabbits from a large burrow for they, knowing the labyrinth well, can play hide-and-seek with it endlessly. Equally, too many ferrets increase the chance of a rabbit being trapped between two, leading to a lay-up. It is always best to start with too few and add more, rather than the reverse. Niblett possibly erred on the generous side, 'If you come to a big earth which you think contains ten or twelve rabbits, and has as many or more outlets, put in four ferrets to begin with, and if they do not move them put in two more.' Thomas would have none of this slap-happy procedure and laid down precise scales which are worth repeating. Small buries, he wrote, have up to five connected holes and some twenty yards of tunnelling. For these one ferret will suffice. Medium size buries have eight to ten holes, thirty to forty yards (27·4–36·6 m) of tunnelling and need two ferrets. Large buries have twelve to fifteen holes, forty to sixty yards (36·6–54·9 m) of tunnelling and need three ferrets. Beyond this Thomas worked on a rule of thumb of one ferret for every ten holes. Thomas was obviously a man who worked by calculation rather than guess work, even to the point of laying down that a good ferret, working good burrows, should bolt six rabbits an hour. If only matters proceeded so smoothly!

Pursuing rabbits through burrows is hard work and ferrets will tire, particularly those which do not normally have an open run for exercise. When a ferret slows up, rest it, for not to do so invites a lay-up. Remember, also, the milk I urged you to bring. A regular drink not only refreshes the ferret, but encourages it to break off a lay-up and pop up for a nip.

We are not quite ready to pop our ferret into the hole, but must consider some way of locating it in the event of a prolonged lay-up. Until recently the only available system was a ferret bell attached to a collar round the neck. This was a small hollow brass bell filled with iron shot, the noise from which indicated the whereabouts of the ferret as it struggled with a live rabbit or tore at a carcass. The system was not, in general, popular. Niblett maintained, 'Any benefit [ferret bells] may possess in the way of signalling the whereabouts of a lying-up ferret is fully counter-balanced by their many disadvantages.' Unfortunately, having roused our interest he did not go on to list them. Harting was more forthcoming, 'Bells are of no use. They only alarm the rabbits, and are not heard in deep burrows.' Thomas, putting the contrary argument, agreed that bells alarmed rabbits and thought highly of the fact. 'Regarding collar and bell, I always use them on a loose ferret because the bell, in my belief, materially assists in putting rabbits' nerves on edge, and makes them easier for the ferret to move and bolt.'

Now the bell has been superseded by a device which has completely revolutionized the sport of ferreting—the electronic 'Bleeper'. The technique of ferreting had continued unchanged for centuries with all the marvels of science making no contribution to greater efficiency in chasing rabbits from their homes with ferrets. In an instant all was changed by the introduction of a miniature, low frequency radio transmitter, which can be fastened around a ferret's neck by a collar. This transmits regular 'bleeps' which can be picked up by a small receiver held by the ferreter. Using this the whereabouts of the ferret can be accurately located in seconds; and even, with practice, the approximate depth forecast. Without exaggeration the use of a locator completely changes the sport; it saves time, boredom, lost ferrets, abandoned rabbits, partly destroyed burrows and the wrath of farmers over badly filled excavations.

The origin of the Bleeper lies with a one-time Norfolk keeper, John Lawrence, who, whilst not inventing the device, conceived the need for it and looked for some existing invention which could be adapted. Various ideas were found wanting, including a G.P.O. line detector, until the TV programme *Tomorrow's World* broadcast a description of a 'bleeping' golf ball, which could be easily traced in the rough. Commercially the golf ball was a failure but Lawrence quickly adapted the idea for ferreting, gave up keepering and now sells Bleepers. The locator has a range of six to eight feet (1·8 to 2·4 m), at least when properly tuned, although I am sure that development will see further improvements. The original transmitter had to be discarded when the power cell ran down after several months. This was superseded by a transmitter with a replaceable battery which, at the time that I write, has the disadvantage of being slightly larger. It is not, however, a major encumbrance to the ferret. Some modest skill is required in its operation but it is easily acquired and then, I repeat, the whole business of ferreting is revolutionized.

At the moment there is a competing device on the market but it is inferior. It is difficult to forecast the future, for whilst the locator is an excellent device this does not necessarily ensure its permanent commercial success. It is already quite expensive, £20 at this time, and if inflation should drive the price beyond the pockets of most ferreters (who are not normally among the wealthiest), the spiral could begin of decreased output putting up unit costs, and so on. For the sake of easier ferreting we must hope that John Lawrence and his Bleeper will thrive. His address, incidentally, is Luton Lodge, Selling, near Faversham, Kent.

At long last we are, in military terms, about to blow the whistle and storm over the top. Armed with our ferrets, coped or not, belled or Bleepered, guns or nets and a mass of ancillary equipment we approach the burrow. Some ferreters prefer to shoot, others to net, and some a combination of both. I deal with both methods later, but the initial procedure is the same. The first rule is silence. Rabbits bolt because their fear of the ferret which appears below ground is stronger than their natural instinct not to leave the burrow in daylight. We noted earlier how even such a relatively trivial matter as unfavourable weather encouraged them to prefer facing the ferret. How much more reluctant will they be to bolt if there are man noises from above. The need to move silently is greater in conditions of frost when hard ground transmits noise and vibrations more than wet, absorbent ground. It is sensible to reconnoitre the burrows several days in advance, note all the entrances and remove any vegetation which will obstruct nets or a clear shot at a bolting rabbit. This done, the ferret can be prepared some yards away and popped in quietly without any need to trample around. Of course, any approach must be from the side and not over the actual roof of the burrow.

As I mentioned earlier the burrows to be worked should be selected and not visited purely by chance. The weather may mean excluding some and favouring others. Or a burrow may have a heavy cover of vegetation, both on and around it and will be better left until the winter frost has cut it down. Most books advise approaching a burrow from downwind to avoid your scent being carried into it, but personally I doubt this is often a danger. There is rarely much movement of air through a burrow and if there was the rabbits would abandon it as draughty. None the less I always follow the rule of working from and waiting for results from downwind, because a rabbit which does not bolt hurriedly, but pauses in the hole to review the situation, will get my scent. Niblett recommends putting the ferret in at a downwind hole, presumably in the expectation that the rabbit's scent will drift down to it. Once again I query the point, but if there is substance in it then there is a good argument for putting the ferret in upwind when its own scent will drift to the rabbit. In this way the rabbit is more likely to have some preliminary warning and bolt rather than be seized by a ferret approaching without warning from downwind, with a subsequent lay-up. Much, of course, will depend on the strength and direction of the wind on the day, but commonsense suggests rabbits do not build burrows with a flow of air through them. Do you open your bedroom window in January?

On the subject of wind and scent, I have a Norfolk friend, David Lyles, who has an interesting theory. Over the years he has observed that rabbits bolt less freely into the wind than away from it. The reason, he suggests, is that ground predators hunt principally by scent, and over the centuries their prey will have developed the instinct to get downwind of them. Hence rabbits bolting with, rather than against the wind. If his thinking is correct it is yet another reason for waiting downwind of the burrow, but—and this is important—not in an obvious position. A rabbit with a ferret just behind will bolt even if you waved a red flag at the entrance. Others, under less pressure, may sit in the entrance for some time and if they spot you will always slip back below. Wherever there is a tree or other cover, stand in front not behind it, and keep quite still. With or without cover it is never sensible to stand directly in front of the holes, but as far to the side as practical. With a small burrow it may be possible to stand so that you cannot be seen by a rabbit until it has actually bolted. Other considerations enter into the question of where to stand. Rabbits rarely bolt aimlessly but with a destination in mind. It may be a nearby burrow or a regular run down a hedgeside or ditch, but some advance thinking will show the likely routes and indicate where best to stand. It is also necessary to have a clear view of a ditch bottom or other route where the ferret could otherwise emerge unseen and wander off.

Earlier I must have shown my state of uncertainty as to whether the ferret should be entered on the up or downwind side of the burrow. Doubtful as I am over this, on one point I am clear; whenever possible insert the ferret at the lowest hole in the burrow. By doing this you increase the chance that, if it does kill, the subsequent lay-up will be shallower than if the entry had been made at a high-level hole and much digging will be saved.

Several other minor points may be conveniently disposed of at this stage. Some people like to take a dog, others do not. Unless it has the ability to distinguish between occupied and unoccupied burrows there is no useful service it can perform other than providing company during a lay-up. Interestingly, those few books that discuss this question all make the point that the dog should be accustomed to ferrets in case it should attack them. None of them have considered the need to accustom the ferrets to the dog! A shooting stick is not a foppish luxury but gives a rare chance to sit down if all is quiet below. Finally, if the spare ferrets are kept in a box, keep it well away from the burrow as the noise of scratching could alarm a rabbit.

Is it better to net or shoot? It is largely a matter of personal preference and circumstances. Netting results in clean, undamaged rabbits but takes considerably longer, even when you are adept at putting down and taking up nets. Additionally a rabbit leaving slowly may see the net and draw back, resulting in a lay-up which would not have occurred with an unobscured hole. However, this only applies where there is a single rabbit at home, for with shooting the noise which attends the first departure alarms those still below. There is, at least so Barkley tells us, a third alternative, for he gives an interesting description of bolting rabbits to a waiting pack of dogs.

Personally, as I ferret for sport rather than meat I prefer to shoot, and tricky work it is too. It is rare to have a clear view of the target for more than a yard or so, particularly with a big burrow where they often just dart from one hole to another. This need for rapid snap shooting does make rabbit shooting to ferrets a potentially dangerous activity and it is certainly no place for several inexperienced Guns. The safest combination is one person working the ferrets and another shooting. More than two, except with an exceptionally large burrow, is dangerous and even with two, care has to be taken over positioning. With hedgerow ferreting two Guns are essential, as one cannot cover both sides and the best arrangement is to stand exactly opposite one another and only fire at a safe angle. An alternative is to have one standing well back from the hedge and the other close, on the opposite side, but some way down the hedge. Rabbits bolted from a hedgerow burrow almost invariably run up or down the hedge and very rarely across the open field. It is highly desirable that the two Guns can see one another and where this is impossible neither should move from his position without warning the other. Rabbits will frequently bolt down a dry ditch, along a thick hedge or along some other route it is impossible to shoot. In this case a short length of netting can be suspended across or even, if the run is confined, a purse net. An alternative is a handkerchief in the run which will divert the rabbit into the open.

Opinions vary on the ideal gun for the job, but what is certain is that the usual combination of gun and cartridge is too powerful and causes excessive damage to the carcass. Sedgwick recommended the ·410 but this is an unnecessarily demanding little gun for such tricky shooting. An open bored 20 bore is excellent, but this is not the normal weapon of the majority. Personally I use my normal game-shooting 12 bore, which is more open bored than my rough shooting gun, with 2-inch cartridges. The shot charge is less than the normal 20 bore and I have the advantage of using a familiar gun. No. 6 or 7 shot is best, although Parker in *Elements of Shooting* recommended no. 4 on the grounds that it caused less damage to the carcass. (You may recall that, earlier, I quoted the Gun who preferred no. 3 shot for covert shooting for the same reason.)

You will remember I mentioned earlier those cases where the rabbit, not hard pressed by the ferret, will come slowly to the entrance and look around. At first thought there is a good case for shooting it there and then and, surprisingly, for he is so sound in his advice, this action is recommended by Niblett. There are, in fact, two major objections. Firstly, you cannot be sure where the ferret is, and you could easily shoot it as well as the rabbit, if only by a chance pellet ricocheting down the hole. (I have several times discovered that rabbits apparently sitting in the hole observing were actually reluctant to emerge because the ferret was firmly attached to their rear.) Secondly, a wounded rabbit can easily kick itself back into the hole and a lay-up then becomes certain. For this last reason you should always give a second barrel to a rabbit which bolts and is only wounded by the first. Even if severely wounded a rabbit will usually scramble into its home burrow somehow, and out of kindness to the rabbit and consideration for your day's programme it is much better to make certain. Good sportsmanship requires that a wounded rabbit which has escaped to a fresh burrow should be dispatched; a commendable attitude which, none the less, carries risks, for a wounded frightened rabbit will be reluctant to bolt again. In fact, Niblett goes so far as to state categorically that a rabbit once bolted and shot at will invariably refuse to bolt again that day. As, in these circumstances, a lay-up is highly probable, it is worth checking that the rabbit is not lying just inside the hole before putting the ferret in. If badly wounded a rabbit will often stop as soon as it reaches safety and will sometimes die almost at once. Cut a stout bramble 'rod', remove all but the last half-dozen thorns and probe gently down the hole with this. If the rabbit is encountered push the rod past, then bring it back slowly, twisting it to entangle the thorns in the fur.

Do not, as a shooting ferreter, be above taking some purse nets for they can be very useful. They can be used to cover the odd hole or two beyond your range of vision or, more frequently, to net holes when there is a lay-up and you must put your gun down. (Rabbits will bolt when you put down your gun with the same consistency that pigeons will appear in view when you leave a decoy hide.)

Netting, although not as exciting as shooting, is a job calling for some skill and offers its own satisfaction. In theory it is possible to surround a very large burrow with a long-net, but in practice the rabbits tend to dart from hole to hole rather than making a clean break. In fact, nearly all netting is done by covering every hole with an individual purse net which, for the benefit of the novice, is a bag net with a draw-cord around the edges. The cord is attached to a peg which is thrust into the ground near a hole, the net draped over it and the bolting rabbit enters the bag and tightens the draw-cord. Attention to detail in setting the net pays. The centre of the net should be in the centre of the hole, otherwise the rabbit may strike the edge of the net, fail to enter the bag and escape round the side. Also the tighter the net is stretched across the hole the less mesh is available for the rabbit to see—fully stretched it looks like a few strands of grass; bunched together in thick clusters it is obvious. The cluster of netting lying on the ground should be arranged so that the outer edge is nearest the hole. In this way the rabbit is running into the bag rather than thrusting underneath it. The peg should not be pushed in vertically, but with the point at a slight angle in the direction of the rabbit's flight. The tug of the rabbit entering the net will then tend to pull the peg further into the ground rather than out. Finally, all vegetation which could foul the smooth operation of the draw-cord should be cleared. It is worth remembering that more than one rabbit can bolt, from different holes, at the same time and a net may have to hold a rabbit for half a minute or so while you deal with another.

When a rabbit hits a net grasp it firmly and, before doing anything else, cover the hole with a fresh net. Only then kill the rabbit and untangle the net. If you have no spare net then stand in the hole until you have freed the net. It is, of course, essential to net all the holes of a burrow, and to ensure this it is wise to net any single hole within ten yards. Little-used holes will also become hidden under twigs, dead leaves and other debris. Nets are easily lost by overlooking them, for by design they are inconspicuous. The best technique is to count them as you put them down and later take them up. For tidiness I fold them to and fro along the length of the peg and then bind their draw-cords around the bundle. Others find an elastic band more effective but I tend to lose them in the hurly-burly of the day.

A good craftsman will also deal with rabbits efficiently. The simplest way of killing them is to hold them up by the back legs with the left hand and chop them behind the ears with the open right hand. Alternatively hold the small of the back with the left hand, whilst holding the rabbit belly down on the left thigh. Place the right hand under the head, with the head in the palm of the hand and two fingers each side of the neck. Pull down and at the same time lever up and back sharply. The neck will break instantly. As soon as time permits, 'leak' it by holding the head in one hand and squeezing the bladder dry with the other. Leg or 'hock' rabbits as soon as possible and then hang them. The right leg should be inserted through the left and the incision in the latter can be made, if no knife is available, by using the rabbit's own teeth. Rabbits are best carried by inserting a stick through the legs or by tying two bundles, by the back legs, and draping them over a shoulder. After they have cooled paunch them. Place your thumb nail a quarter-inch (6 mm) up the knife blade to avoid too deep a cut puncturing the intestines, and slit the belly from between the legs for some three to four inches (75–100 mm). Do not keep the rabbit on its back and fight gravity but hold it by the neck and let it help. The more adventurous can try the technique of holding the two extremities of the rabbit with the belly upwards and placing the thumbs in the back and pushing. This forces the various organs into prominence, when a vigorous swing should project them into the hedge. However, I must stress that the operation needs doing with manly firmness—any timidity sees the contents, which appear to be attached to the body by bloodstained elastic, returning at the end of the swing. The less exciting method is to insert two fingers into the cavity, hook them behind the stomach and pull both it and the various attachments out with a firm, smooth movement. It is normal to leave the liver and kidneys in and the heart should be retained, being much favoured by ferrets.

As the vitally important matter of lay-ups warrants its own chapter, there remains only the after-thought of the various creatures ferrets will encounter in rabbit holes besides rabbits, and what the outcome will be. In opposing muzzling Thomas listed the possibilities of encounters with rats, cats and little owls. With a rat the outcome will almost always be a bolted rat or a dead one. A little owl would not, I think, face a ferret but a cat is another matter. There are various accounts of cats being bolted by ferrets and while I do not doubt these, I am a little surprised. There are many reported instances of ferrets bolting foxes, although it is difficult to imagine why as the only creature approximating to a ferret in the fox's experience would be a stoat, and, in view of the size difference, one would have thought the stoat much more likely to be afraid of the fox. Evidence that not all foxes are afraid of ferrets appears in Carnegie's *Practical Trapping*, in which he relates an occasion when, inadvertently, he put a ferret into some rocks containing a fox. Quite soon the fox emerged with the dead ferret in its mouth, dropped it and ran off. Ferrets must often encounter weasels and stoats underground, but being so closely related, they never appear to fight. Only last spring one of our ferrets bolted a stoat from a small burrow on Skye. We marked it to a nearby burrow and, for interest, inserted the ferret whereupon the stoat again bolted quickly.

CHAPTER NINE

Lay-ups and their Solutions

Lay-ups are to ferreting as a maggot in a sweet apple or measles to childhood—a blot on an otherwise happy experience. Occasional lay-ups cannot be avoided, but a study of the different methods of solving them will help to cut the inconvenience to a minimum. However, before we consider this sombre subject we will raise our spirits with a relevant extract from Barkley. To be fair it is not strictly concerned with solving lay-ups but the subject is sufficiently related to justify inclusion. Barkley had been walking in the country when he spotted a ferreter at work and stayed to watch in the hope of learning a 'wrinkle'. 'I saw at once that three of the latter [dogs] were very good and up to their work; but there was a fourth, a nondescript sort of beast with a long tail, that appeared quite useless; and I observed with amusement that directly the man put a ferret into a hole, the dog tucked its tail tight between its legs and went and stood well out in the field. I asked the man why he kept such a useless beast, and with a chuckle he answered, "Well, mate, I'll own up he ain't much to boast on for rat-killing, nor yet for his looks, but he has his use like some other of we h'ugly ones. You see, sir, I've got one or two ferrets as won't come out of a 'ole, but stand a peeping at the h'entrance and waste a lot of time. Then that 'ere dawg comes in useful. I catches him, lifts him up, and sticks his bushy tail down to the ferret, who catches tight hold, and I draws it out. Nothing ain't made for nothing, and I expect that dawg was made for drawing ferrets."'

The first principle in solving lay-ups is to reduce their occurrence to a minimum and, in this context, I will quote from Thomas, who stipulates that it is essential for a Gun to remain hidden from sight downwind of the bury, in absolute quiet. 'A rabbit pausing in the mouth of a hole prior to bolting will, on the least suspicion of an enemy outside, remain in the bury preferring his chances of dodging the known enemy to facing an unknown one in the open. *Fifteen out of sixteen kills by ferrets arise from this cause.*' I think he overstates his case, for if it were true, then in fifteen lay-ups out of sixteen, or at least a high proportion, we would first see the rabbit appear at a hole and then withdraw. We do not, and I am satisfied that the usual cause is simply that the ferret either takes the rabbit by surprise (after all we know they spend much of the day asleep) or traps it in a cul-de-sac. None the less many lay-ups are caused by ferreters not following Thomas's instructions.

The risk of a lay-up increases with the size of the burrow and the novice, and indeed the experienced ferreter when time is short, will be wise to avoid large burrows. Commonsense will tell you not to ferret close to dusk. Single-entrance bolt holes are a near certain formula for lay-ups, although the subsequent dig should be short. Lay-ups are also more frequent for those men who pride themselves upon owning and working large ferrets, forgetting that the object is not to kill the rabbit but to drive it out.

It was a common belief among old-timers that ferrets killed rabbits by forcing them into a dead-end, blocking the hole with their bodies and suffocating them. The prospect is ludicrous, but the belief must have been founded on some practical experience. Several rabbits will sometimes be trapped in a cul-de-sac, and in their terror of the ferret cases may have occurred where those at the back have been crushed to the point of suffocation. While touching on the past it is an interesting, although cruel, fact that some old-time ferreters would break off the canine teeth of the ferrets to prevent them killing.

Not all lay-ups are a voluntary act on the part of the ferret. In a tussle in a cul-de-sac it is possible for the ferret to become shut in by the carcass of the rabbit it has just killed. In time it can eat through, which is another reason for not muzzling.

The ideal solution to lay-ups often appeared in shooting books of the last century, which were written on the presumption that anyone who could afford to buy the book could afford the cheap labour assistance of the times. Just 'leave a lad to wait for the ferret and move onto the next burrow.' Unfortunately the price of 'lads' nowadays is such that we must do without them and I will pass on to a summary of the various ingenious devices for recovering a ferret.

How long you wait before taking action depends on the size of the burrow and the number of ferrets operating, but with small to medium burrows and one or two ferrets, if nothing happens for a quarter of an hour, a lay-up is indicated. If two of you are shooting, only one should investigate while the other remains at the ready. If you are alone, net the holes. To a large degree the procedure followed will depend on whether the ferret is fitted with a Bleeper or not. If it is location will be a simple matter, but even then it has either to be enticed out or dug for. Whether fitted with a locator or not there are various techniques to be followed before reaching for the spade, but the advantage of a locator is that your efforts can be concentrated more accurately.

One device that I have found very effective is to lure the ferret out by paunching a rabbit and placing it at a hole entrance. This will not entice it from a fresh kill but a ferret which is not hungry (remember, please, my earlier advice about feeding normally in the morning) will not stay long on a dead carcass and once it begins to move around will pick up the new scent. Place the carcass in an upwind hole and peg it or the ferret may drag it below. Thomas goes a stage further and suggests rubbing the rabbit around the inside of the hole and then dragging it into the field. The ferret will then follow the scent into the field where it can be clearly seen, which permits you to go off and ferret a nearby burrow whilst waiting. Personally I think an experienced ferret would turn back at the hole, assuming the rabbit to have bolted; and I would rather make sure it found the carcass.

An elaboration on this theme is to tie a rabbit's innards around a hazel rod and push it down various holes, leaving it in each for a few minutes. This is particularly effective if you have located the ferret. More aggressive methods exist. If the ferret is not too deep you can simply thump the ground with the spade, hoping that either curiosity or fright will move it from the carcass or trapped rabbit. Thomas suggests removing the shot from a cartridge and firing the gun in the lowest upwind hole of the burrow. This, he claims, will invariably bring the ferret up within three minutes if the burrow is of small or medium size. (Thomas, you will note, tends to categorical statements!) Charles St. John in *Wild Sports of the Highlands* supported the theory but urged the use of tobacco smoke, saying, 'Tobacco smoke will also bring a ferret out of a rabbit-hole, when everything else fails to do so.' Carnegie in *Practical Trapping* agreed to the principle of stinking the poor ferret out but did the job more thoroughly. All the holes but one had to be closed, a 'spitz devil' lit within the open hole and then this also was blocked. Five minutes later the burrow was opened when the ferret 'will generally be glad to come out.' In spite of its awesome name the smell generator was simply a charge of powder placed on paper, moistened and rolled into a ball. The moisture would slow the burning and, I imagine, create more fumes. Niblett took the technique a stage further. His ferret evictor was to 'Take some strips of rough, thick brown paper cut in lengths of 12 in. [30·5 cm] by 2 in. [5 cm] wide. Then pound together in a mortar twelve parts of nitre and one of cayenne pepper, and work this up into a thick solution with water. Lay two slips of the paper on a board, paint them with the solution, place one upon the other, and repeat the process till six are similarly treated; roll them up, dry them, and keep them in a tin box for future use.' From then on the method was the same as Carnegie's.

Everitt offers the usual tips, but it occurred to me that the non-sporting walker in the countryside might be alarmed if he saw you following his advice to 'Jump about on the outside of the earth, and beat the ground with the flat of a shovel or spade.'

Of course, none of this may be necessary if you followed the recommendation to train your ferret to come to call. An alternative is to imitate the squeal of a rabbit in distress by sucking through the lips.

If none of these measures work then you must dig; but, unless it is a short bolt hole, it is a waste of time to dig unless you know the approximate location of the ferret. Once again I make the point that a Bleeper revolutionizes the whole business, but even without it all is not lost. If the rabbit is not dead it is sometimes possible to hear the ferret scratching and tussling by placing your ear to a hole. A favourite device of old-timers was a 'warreners' telephone': a five- or six-foot (1·5–1·8 m) metal rod which was driven into the ground where the ferret was thought to be. This picked up sounds below ground which could be heard by placing an ear to the end of the rod. Samuel and Lloyd recommend using such a rod as a probe to trace the course of the hole but I would have thought the risk of piercing the ferret is too great to justify the method.

The next step, and a very common one, is to use a liner—that is, another ferret with a long line attached to a collar. This is sent down, finds the site of the kill and, guided by the line, you dig down to it. Convention demands that the liner is a hob, the idea being that being stronger, it will drive the working ferret, usually a jill, off the carcass. Another advantage of a strong liner is that if the carcass is not far from the entrance it may be possible to pull both ferret and rabbit out gradually.

If you have some idea where the laid-up ferret is put the liner in at the nearest hole. If not, use the hole where the ferret was originally inserted. Keep the line taut and if the ferret doubles back recover line at once or it may catch around a root or stone. In order that you know the distance of the carcass from the point of insertion of the liner the line must be marked at regular intervals—every two feet is a practical distance. Many people tie knots, but these are liable to catch in an obstruction and it is better to sew in coloured tassels. As the liner moves in have your companion watch the nearby holes. He may see the line passing and this will save much digging time. An orange cord for the liner shows up well. Once the liner remains static for a minute or two you can assume it has found the carcass, and a taut line will often confirm this by tugs and twitches.

Before getting down to the actual digging it is worth mentioning a tip of Thomas's to overcome the risk that a line may become caught up in a difficult burrow, where digging proves impossible. He suggests all lines should, before use, be well soaked in saltpetre. Then if one becomes snagged it can be lit and will smoulder, in the same manner as a fuse, until the ferret is freed.

The favourite tool for digging is a slim, rounded spade, often called a 'graft'. (Perhaps the origin of the description 'hard-graft' for tiring work?) Niblett, as always the authority, specified an iron, a foot (30 cm) long, 6½ inches (16·5 cm) across the top, 5 inches (12·7 cm) across the bottom, and with a handle of 2 feet 2 inches (66 cm) long. Grander implements were also standard at one time. Barkley recommended a spade with a ten-foot (3 m) handle and a steel hook at the end. The long handle permitted deep digging and the hook was used to lift the rabbit, hopefully with the ferret clinging on. In Tommy Turner's part of England the digging-staff, as he called it, was more modest—only 7 feet 6 inches (2·3 m) or thereabouts.

Part of the art of digging is to reduce work to the minimum. Cut a hazel or bramble rod and push it down the hole as far as possible—with a straight hole this can be a considerable distance. Have your companion lie above where you think the hole runs then vibrate the stick up and down. With a little adjustment he should be able to locate its position. Then dig a narrow trench at right angles to the direction of the hole and about two feet (61 cm) long. When you strike the hole widen your excavation to permit the stick to be inserted and the operation repeated. If the stick suggests a fork, dig down at this point and check which branch the line takes. When the stick touches the rabbit or ferret you should find a few hairs on it. Dig down short of the point and with care as it is very easy to injure the ferret. (The indicators on your line will give an accurate distance.) Dig below the level of the hole and come in *under* the rabbit and ferret. This reduces both the risk of striking the ferret with the spade and causing the roof to cave in and suffocate it. If you have recovered the original loose ferret then grasp the rabbit first, for it may not be dead. However, if both the liner and the loose ferret are on it, take the loose ferret first. As you remove the rabbit place your foot in the hole, for the spot is probably a dead-end and there may well be other rabbits beyond.

Afterwards take care to replace all the disturbed soil and leave the area in a tidy state. Writing of the warreners on the Elveden estate, Turner said they would place the top sod on one side of the hole they were digging and the earth on the other. Afterwards the earth went back, the sod was replaced and trodden and it was difficult to see where the ground had been disturbed.

If after trying everything you cannot recover the ferret and time or failing light compels you to leave it, block up every hole but one and dig the open carrying box into this, with plenty of hay, and, if possible, a drink. With luck the ferret will be in it when you return the next day. If you have only a carrying bag, thrust this into the hole, cover it with hay or straw and then block up. A better arrangement is to make a practice of taking on your ferreting expeditions a ferret trap, which to avoid the nuisance of carrying it everywhere, can be left in the vehicle unless needed. A wire rat- or cat-trap will do and this should be baited with some rabbit and left near a hole, the others all being blocked. A fairly sizeable trap is best as it allows you to place a good pile of straw in one end to keep the ferret warm after capture. In cold weather this will not be sufficient and the trap needs covering with sacks or some other protection. If you are a frequent ferreter it would be well worthwhile building a wooden box trap. Everitt took great pains over recapturing lost ferrets, using box traps with sleeping quarters, milk and food and said his ferrets knew the appearance of this trap and invariably went to it. As an additional aid he dragged the entrails of a rabbit along the ground from the open hole to the trap.

He also mentioned a form of pitfall trap made by digging a pit, on the windward side of the main entrance to the burrow, about fifteen inches square and thirty inches deep with smooth walls. A nest of hay, grass or bracken is formed in the bottom and a thin stick is stuck upright in the centre of the pit to a height of six inches (15 cm) or so above the level of the pit's edge. The bait is tied to the stick and then branches laid across the pit and covered with grass to conceal the hole. The theory is that the ferret, in trying to reach the bait, tumbles through the holes in the branches.

Ferrets have been credited with a homing instinct, and Harting reports that Dr. G. J. Romanes, in his book on Animal Instinct (1882), stated that he lost a ferret about a mile from home which returned several days later. Of course, this could have been pure chance but there are similar reports in *The Field* of 25 January and 1 and 8 February 1873; 23 and 30 January 1886, and 17 March 1888. Logically it is difficult to accept such an instinct. Most domesticated animals have ample opportunities to find their bearings by constantly moving, or being moved, around an area. And wild creatures, particularly birds, have their faculties for navigation sharpened by constant movement. But the ferret spends his time either in a hutch, down a burrow, or being conveyed between the two in a dark box. If, indeed, ferrets have a homing instinct it is yet one further example of instinctive powers beyond our present comprehension.

CHAPTER TEN

On a Shining Night

There is an old country song, *Rabbits and Hares*, which begins:

> My tykes o'the entry
> Since fortune affords
> The partridge for gentry,
>   the pheasant for lords,
> While Kings and their cousins
> Goes foreign for bears,
> 'Tis rabbits for us 'uns,
> 'Tis rabbits and hares!
> *Rabbits an' hares*
>   All unawares.
> Rabbits for us 'un, lads,
> Rabbits an' hares!

But not, for most of the men who sang it, the legal taking. Once, at the dawn of the world as we know it, all game was available to whoever could take it. When the first tribe laid claim to its own territory and the first outsider slipped in to net a boar, spear a fish or drop a rock on a grazing deer, poaching began. Had the private ownership of game coincided with man's arrival on earth, then poaching and not prostitution would be the oldest profession, although not, I will concede, by many minutes.

The motives behind poaching are not always simple, consisting of a complex weave of need, greed and excitement; the precise pattern depending on the individual and circumstances. Socially it has never been regarded as a serious offence by the normal populace, and even now there is a distinct 'them and us' attitude, in which 'us' is the working man and 'them' the landowners. Admittedly the anti-poaching laws, as I show soon, have been severe, but this is an expression not of the attitude of the nation generally but of the influence the landowning classes had on the process of law making. Looking back over more than a century of great social upheaval it is difficult for us to appreciate the extent of the gulf between the rich and the poor. A few extracts from *Sporting Scenes and Country Characters*, written in 1840 by 'Martingale', will help to illustrate the point. The author's position in life is clearly stamped by the beginning of his chapter on pheasant shooting, 'Merrily bounds the heart of the true old sportsman as, on the first of October, he leaves his mansion . . .' This was the manner of man who governed and what was his view of the poacher? 'Having little sympathy with his fellowmen, and less of all the obligations due to society, he pursues his course with a fixed determination of purpose and a recklessness of consequence peculiar to himself, and worthy of a better cause' and he is 'the frequenter of the tap-room, the alehouse, and the beer-shop.' Were you so unfortunate as to be appearing before this gentleman after being found with several of the squire's pheasants, your knowledge of his opinion of poachers would not cheer you. But there is worse to come. 'In prosecuting his lawless occupations amid these midnight and destructive plunder-scenes,—where all sense of shame and degredation is wholly disregarded, where passion is excited to the highest pitch, and where desperation is so far in the ascendant as to leave behind not only traces of the greatest destruction of the preserves, but of bleeding wounds, and even of the murder of his fellow creatures.' To leave us in no doubt that he considers the average poacher a potential murderer there also appears, 'If he be suddenly pounced upon, the loss of life is almost inevitable.' Yet 'Martingale' was no fanatic, but a decent, responsible, feeling member of the upper classes.

To gain a clear picture of nineteenth-century poaching we must draw a sharp distinction between local resident poachers and raiding gangs from outside the area. The behaviour of local men was rarely extreme for, particularly if they were family men, all the normal cross-interests of a small, restricted community bore upon them. Outside gangs were another matter and their behaviour provided justification for harsh laws. 'Martingale' on gangs wrote, 'In the case of a determined attack from the keeper and his watchers, the former is marked for almost certain destruction, particularly if his previous informations have inflicted punishment on any one of the party of poachers.' Although we suspect 'Martingale' of exaggeration, there is corroboration elsewhere; consider Jefferies: 'The raiders, who came in gangs armed with guns and shoot in the preserves, are usually the scum of manufacturing towns.' Or Sheail: 'Poachers often hunted in gangs, and such towns as Brandon in the Breckland became a popular refuge for them.' Or, again from Sheail: 'The Game Acts of 1828 and 1831 dealt much more severely with gangs of poachers, who were much more efficient in raiding game preserves, and often resorted to violence and even murder to avoid being caught. Gangs of miners and mill-workers often fought running battles with keepers on estates near industrial towns and villages. During periods of depression, many bands of starving men ravaged preserves within a wide radius of large centres of population, like the colliers who denuded estates of game up to twelve miles of Manchester.'

The sharp distinction between raiding gangs from a distance and local men no doubt attracted different responses from the keeper. The gangs would be both feared and hated and would be opposed to the full, but it would be interesting to journey back in time and discover the keeper's attitude to local poachers. They were, after all, both from the same social group, normally united against the wealthy. One suspects the keeper's efforts were concerned not so much towards protecting his master's pheasants as to protecting his own job. However, this may be far too cynical a view, for this was an age when loyalty and associated attitudes had not been debased—it took a World War and millions of casualties before the common man seriously questioned the position of the ruling classes.

There was certainly a case for sympathizing with the casual poacher. At the turn of the century a farm labourer would be earning about eighteen shillings a week, paying four or five shillings rent for his cottage and raising a family on the residue. The temptation to poach, either to eat or sell, was strong, for game was fetching good prices and no questions were asked. Nor did the man who was caught and imprisoned suffer any social stigma from his contemporaries. It was all part of the business of surviving in an underprivileged world.

Not all early poaching was done for gain. In his classical *Diary*, Colonel Peter Hawker gives an account, both interesting and amusing, of a day's poaching in 1808. Leading a party of nearly twenty he stormed the woods of an unfortunate Parson Bond who had offended his assailants by never offering anyone a day's shooting and filling his wood with man-traps and dog-gins. In the midst of the shooting the parson appeared and 'did not know which way to run', for 'not a word could be heard for the cries of "Mark", "Dead" and "Well done", interspersed every moment with bang bang and the yelping of barrack curs.' At last, 'The Parson having eased himself by a vomit, began to speak more coherently and addressed himself to those who, being liable to an action of trespass, were obliged to stand in the footpath, and take the birds as they flew over.' One wonders whether the Colonel's neighbours of the time found him quite so enjoyable a character as we do, protected as we are by well over a century.

Nowadays poaching and poachers are pale shadows of the past, the incentive of need gradually eroded by rising living standards. Myxomatosis dealt the final blow to the man who poached rabbits for profit, reducing numbers to the level where the reward fell far short of justifying the effort. Rabbit poaching now is mainly confined to the quiet fellow seeking one for the pot and others, mainly youngsters, doing it more for the excitement than the bag. If, up to now, I have written lightly of poaching, seeming almost to approve, then let me correctly state my position. Poaching for substantial gain, showing no respect for game, keepers or countryside, is straightforward stealing and entirely reprehensible. Poaching for the pot is also stealing, but understandable, and in cases of genuine need, worthy of sympathy. If one accepts this philosophy it is only a small step to excusing the man who poached not just to feed his family but to sell the surplus to clothe them and provide other comforts. It is difficult for us to look back from the relative security of the present day and form a balanced judgement, but if my children were literally hungry and cold and poaching would ease their plight then I would poach.

For those interested in looking more deeply into poaching there has recently been a spate of reprints of old out-of-print books.

Some suggest a ne'er-do-well character, unwilling to buckle down to steady work and only too pleased to glamorize his petty thieving. Others carry with them the ever-present shadow of insecurity and poverty which drove a man to poach in spite of the heavy penalties. A rough dividing line between the two groups is that men in one poached because they wanted to and in the other because they had to. The problem with finding a really genuine book by a representative poacher is that no one who could write was ever likely to have poached through sheer need. Quite the best, in my view, is *I Walked by Night*. This was written by an anonymous Norfolk man who was born about 1858 and as an old man of seventy-five jotted his memories down in an exercise book. This reached the hands of Lilias Rider Haggard who had the skill and sensitivity to edit it into a readable manuscript, still retaining the qualities of strength, warmth and pride that characterized the 'King of the Norfolk poachers'.

A consideration of poaching may be neatly divided into two aspects: the techniques and the penalties. We will start with the latter, as a knowledge of the punishments awaiting failure adds a sense of apprehension to a consideration of the former.

It is difficult to trace the legal position with regard to rabbit poaching prior to the nineteenth century. We know that William the Conqueror, who was fond of sport, ruthlessly cleared the inhabitants from large stretches of countryside to add to his royal chases, and the ultimate extreme was reached in 1209 when King John prohibited the pursuit and destruction of all game. This was modified in 1389 by an Act of Parliament prohibiting killing rabbits and 'other gentlemen's game', except by persons having certain property qualifications. A not dissimilar Act of 1621, limited to Scotland, restricted the right to kill game to the owners of more than one ploughgate of land—that is, 130 acres (52·6 h)—although, as a privilege, tenants were permitted *to kill rabbits* in the daytime. Both these Acts, by their wording, make it plain that rabbits were regarded as game, and the latter Act also contains the first indication of a strong trend for the law to distinguish sharply between killing rabbits by day and by night.

By the reign of Henry VIII the buying and selling of game was prohibited, although this restriction may have applied only to pheasants and partridges as in the second year of the reign of

James I an Act extended the prohibition to deer and hare. Further Acts in the reigns of William and Mary and Anne imposed further restrictions. These prohibitions related to trading in game, but it would be wrong to assume that the ordinary man could kill rabbits as long as he did not sell them. Various Acts laid down the required qualifications for killing game, but the main one was that of Charles II. The right was generally restricted to those who had an estate of inheritance in real property of the clear yearly value of £100, or an estate for life or for ninety-nine years or more of the clear yearly value of £150. There were others eligible, all persons of privilege.

All the legislation enacted over the centuries had one common purpose—to preserve the sport and the food that naturally emanated from it for those in a position of power. It was for the common man a harsh and unalterable situation. The laws were both made and administered either by the landowners or those closely connected to them. As a result the penalties for poaching were excessive and inhumane. By the nineteenth century a combination of the birth of true democracy and a slowly awakening social conscience was causing the ruling classes to examine many aspects of society and one, relatively unimportant, corner was the Game Laws. In fact the century saw a spate of legislation either aimed directly at or involving the rabbit, but the various laws passed fall into two separate groups—those aimed at eliminating the rabbit and those intended to eliminate rabbit poaching. (The irony of these conflicting objectives will not have escaped you.) Those directed against the rabbit can be left until later.

By 1828 the pressures had increased to the point where a Committee of the House of Lords produced a report recommending changes in the Game Laws. Their proposals were far reaching and, condensed to the bare essentials, were:

A. That the law should be altered to permit the sale and purchase of game.

B. That the right to kill game should be extended to many more people than the then very small minority. (In general an occupier of more than ten acres should be given such right and he should have the right to permit any other person to sport.)

C. That, as granting the right to sell game automatically places a value on such game, it should be adequately protected against poaching by sufficiently strong legislation.

And finally, and of interest to us:

D. That as the practice of night poaching by large gangs had much increased in recent years, leading in numerous cases to murder and other grevious offences, and the law dealing with such poaching was inadequate, it should be revised.

The proposal to lift the restrictions against selling and buying game were simply an appreciation of the extensive and flourishing black market then existing in game. An expanding middle class could afford to eat better and the inns, posting-stables and stage coaches were the link between the rural poachers and the illicit town market.

Parliament acted swiftly and the first legislation to emerge from the report was the Night Poaching Act of 1828. It was, you will not be surprised to learn, lengthy, and trying to extract from it those aspects concerned with rabbits has been one of the more exacting tasks of this book. (I would point out, in defence of the law, that while the virtues of short and simple laws are obvious to the layman an attempt to compile them soon becomes bogged down in providing for the inevitable variation in circumstances. For example, when is 'night'? Or if there are several poachers, need they all enter enclosed land? And so on.) Of greatest interest to us are the penalties. For a first conviction for rabbit poaching at night the offender could receive up to three months hard labour; for a second conviction up to six months; and for a third conviction up to two years hard labour or, at the discretion of the court, to be transported beyond seas for seven years. And this less than 150 years ago for poaching rabbits! The last penalty of up to two years, hard labour or seven years' transportation also applied, irrespective of whether there were previous convictions or not, where any offender 'shall assault or offer any violence with any gun, crossbow, fire-arms, bludgeon, stick, club or any other offensive weapon whatsoever'. Age does not appear to have had any legal effect on the penalties, as the central character of *I Walked by Night* did a month's hard labour in Norwich Castle, at the age of fifteen, for snaring a rabbit.

In 1844 the Act was strengthened in several ways, not least by extending its provisions to any person unlawfully taking any game or rabbits (note that we now see a distinction between game and rabbits) by night on any public road, highway or path. At this time the threat from armed gangs must have grown, for a further variation laid down that if three or more persons unlawfully entered land for the purpose of taking game or rabbits, and any such person was armed with—and then followed the usual list—then the penalty would be transportation for not more than fourteen years or less than seven years, or not more than three years' hard labour.

The Night Poaching Act of 1828 only dealt with a few specialized recommendations of the House of Lords report but the great majority of the remainder appeared in the Game Act of 1831. In keeping with the proposals of the report the two major changes were that anyone holding the appropriate certificate could now buy and sell game, and the old requirement for a person to have 'qualifications' before being permitted to kill game were abolished. There were other provisions—many others—including the right of Lords of manors to appoint gamekeepers (such appointments to be registered with a clerk of the peace), but these two were to revolutionize the future of the sport of shooting. The Act did not, however, make life any easier for rabbit poachers. Indeed, in many ways it made it harder for it cleaned up a muddle of piecemeal legislation from the past and made it easier for the prosecution to secure convictions. At the same time the strong feeling that had arisen against organized poaching by gangs of townees found expression in stiff penalties, which fell just as heavily on the back of the usually less dangerous rural poacher.

Naturally the Act contained innumerable variations, some obvious and some not. Consider, if you can, the reason for 24 & 25 Vict., c. 96, 'Provided that nothing in this section contained shall affect any person taking or killing in the day-time any rabbits on any sea-bank or river-bank in the county of Lincoln, so far as the tide shall extend, or within one furlong of such bank'. Preservation of the banks?—we will probably never know.

In spite of the weight of legislation erected to contain them the poaching fraternity must have operated very successfully, for 1862 saw the Poaching Prevention Act. Essentially the purpose of this was to give to the police the power to search any person who they had good cause to suspect was coming from land where he had been unlawfully in pursuit of game. The police have no power to search a person who they suspect is setting off on a poaching expedition; the right is directed against persons 'coming from land', always provided the authorities have reasonable suspicion. The right extends to any 'cart or other conveyance', which latter description adequately covers the motor car—a contrivance uninvented when the Act was drafted.

No doubt the Act owed its origin to numerous frustrating occasions when poachers were detected but left the ground before they could be apprehended. Once on the public highway the powers of the police were limited and these new powers must have been an extremely useful extension. By previous standards the penalties were mild; a fine not exceeding £5 and the forfeit of game, guns, nets and 'engines'.

Coming practically up to date, a 1960 amendment to the Game Laws substantially increased the power of the courts and police in relation to poaching offences. For example, the police can now enter private land without invitation if they have reasonable grounds to believe there is a poacher at work. Any poacher so apprehended can be arrested and any game or gun found may be seized. Finally we have the Firearms Act 1968, one of the provisions of which makes it an offence for any person who has a firearm with him to enter or be on any private land without permission.

From the foregoing you will gather that the sheer quantity of legislation which can be brought to bear on the poacher has not diminished; in fact, it has increased. What has altered is the attitude of the courts. A century or so ago the magistrate was probably a landowner, and almost certainly was very hostile to poachers. Now many courts treat poachers lightly.

Having covered the penalties we can now look at the techniques of the poacher. Ferreting with nets has the virtue of being quiet, and provided the right burrows are selected, a poacher is out of sight and fairly motionless. Its disadvantages are that it is not highly productive; night ferreting is difficult; and the appearance of a keeper means abandoning the ferret and probably the nets. In general, it was, and is, the method of the countryside equivalent of the petty thief; the big-timers, the High Street bank raiders, as it were, used the long-net. I write 'used' because since myxomatosis, rabbit numbers have not justified this somewhat complex operation. Payne-Gallwey, writing in the Badminton Library's *Shooting*, said that poachers using long-nets would sometimes get two to three hundred rabbits in a single night, and suggested the only remedy was to lay thorns in profusion at places where a net was likely to be used. Harting recommended the same technique, although his second suggestion of driving the rabbits in at 10.00 p.m. and 1.00 a.m. was the more certain protection, albeit less popular with the keepers.

A Poacher's Tale follows the same pattern as *I Walked by Night* in that a practised author has moulded the story of a poacher, in this case the author being A. T. Curtis and the poacher Fred Speakman. The period is too close to our time for the story to have the nostalgia and atmosphere of the Norfolk masterpiece, but it contains many interesting pieces on rabbit poaching. On long-netting he describes how he and his accomplices would drive the rabbits to the net by tying a tin can, part-filled with stones, in the middle of a long length of strong string. In this way two men could drive a field by each walking in the shelter of a hedge and pulling the string to and fro between them. Like other tales in the book it sounds somewhat impractical and I suspect owes as much to a lively imagination as regular usage.

Charles Row in his *A Practical Guide to the Game Laws* (1907), gives an amusing account of an auction in which a local court entered a large accumulation of long-nets, the result of a long period of confiscation from local poachers. The original owners attended, expecting to re-purchase their old favourites, but Row and his friends, foreseeing this, sent an agent to outbid them, taking the view that even if the price was high it would be cheaper than letting them return to the poaching fraternity.

Speakman described a method of taking rabbits without a net or any other device. Towards dusk, when he is less likely to be seen, a poacher will visit a popular burrow and mark every hole with white stones or pieces of crockery. On the next windy night he returns, after midnight, with a companion and a good armful of dry hay. Each hole, easily spotted by its white marker, is then blocked by screwing tight balls of hay into position, an arm's-length down. One man then hides close to the burrow, the other walks in the rabbits, and as they dash into what is now a cul-de-sac, the waiter hauls them out. As a method it has the advantage that there is little or no evidence by dawn, and it is difficult to prove poaching against a man caught with a bundle of hay.

It was common practice for keepers to turn out a few white rabbits and the disappearance of one or more of these obvious markers would be a sign of poaching. In fact, the more wily poachers would free any such rabbit taken by net, although this precaution was denied those poachers who worked with gin or snare. Speakman had a not very endearing method of attracting buck rabbits to his gins in spring. Recognizing that the urge to breed was foremost in the bucks' instincts, he would kill a doe, skin it and 'scrape up the loose earth from the little latrines that rabbits scoop out for themselves, and rub the earth round inside the skin'. This earth was then scattered over the gin and, he claimed, proved an irresistible attraction.

Poaching rabbits with free-ranging dogs has always appealed to poachers as it is quick, quiet and, until the kill occurs, there is no proof that any crime is intended. Jefferies wrote, 'The "mouchers" sneak about the hedgerows on Sundays with lurcher dogs, and snap up a rabbit or a hare; they do not do much damage except near great towns, where they are very numerous.' And the same author on the subject of gypsies, 'They are adept at poaching, and each van is usually accompanied by a couple of dogs.' Jefferies also wrote of the practice of poachers' touring the countryside in a pony and trap, complete with two or three dogs. It was, he suggested, an ideal combination. Trotting quietly along the roads they could not be arrested yet, from their high seat, they had an excellent view over the hedges, and when rabbits were spotted, could carry out the course and be away rapidly.

The lurcher was very much the poacher's dog, and it is a sign of the times that they are quite scarce nowadays. Appropriately, in Romany the name lurcher means to rob or plunder and it is the gypsies who have been the most prolific breeders of this rather remarkable strain, which combines speed with intelligence. The origin was a cross between sheepdog and greyhound, and although there are a variety of alternative crosses, this combination has always been favourite, particularly with a three-quarter greyhound content. Other crosses have included deerhound, saluki, Bedlington, cattle dog, and curly and flat-coated retrievers.

Although in breeding lurchers the main criterion is speed, stamina, both in running and in tolerating hard weather, is also important. To this latter end a thick wiry coat was often sought, and the characteristic is seen at its best in the so-called Norfolk lurcher; a greyhound cross with the cattle dogs used for herding cattle to Smithfield market. Where smaller dogs are desired a whippet is often substituted for the greyhound, but lurchers from a whippet cross are less fast. A popular cross often found in the south, but rarely elsewhere, is the greyhound cross with the saluki.

There have been many remarkable accounts of the almost uncanny relationships existing between gypsies and their lurchers and, even if we discount for exaggeration, that which remains is still impressive. Reputedly they are trained to work quietly on the field side of a hedge while their master walks innocently along the road. Additional assets include the ability to return straight home to a particular whistle and never to bring a hare or rabbit to their owner when a stranger is in view. Perhaps the first-ever mention of a lurcher was by John Casus, who in 1576 wrote *Of Englishe Dogges* and reported that the most popular breed of dog for taking rabbits was a 'tumbler', which was smaller than a hound and often referred to as a mongrel greyhound.

Regrettably but understandably, the defence of the keeper and landowner against poaching dogs was to take measures against the dog rather than its owner. Sheail reported that a standard practice in the warren was to suspend barbed wire between stakes, high enough to allow the rabbits to pass under but capable of severely injuring a pursuing dog. The nineteenth-century veterinary surgeon Richard Lawrence in his *The Complete Farrier and British Sportsman* (1831), on the subject of poaching dogs, wrote, 'Some recommend placing spring-guns at dusk, or dark, in the fields where hares feed (clover or turnips is the most likely), about the height to shoot a dog; or at gate-ways, several dog-spills, or spikes, set in a line about a rod or two in the field; if it joins a wood, set one up in every file, about a rod in; one may be placed about nine inches above the steepers of a hedge, as a dog generally leaps over when a hare takes the muise. A dog running against either of these engines, would certainly be deterred from ever running again, if it did not kill him.' Quite so! Lawrence also quoted in detail an action tried at the assizes in Oxford in 1814, in which a Mr. Dean tried to recover the value of his dog which had killed itself on a dog-spear set in a wood belonging to Sir William Clayton, Bart. In the course of the evidence it was proved that dog-spears were commonly set close to public foot-paths.

Even in this century the practice of suspending barbed wire in the likely route of coursing dogs took place, for Tommy Turner mentions it in his *Memoirs of a Gamekeeper*.

Patrick Chalmers gave a fascinating account in *The Frequent Gun* (1928) of watching a lurcher at work, although, as I have said before, no tale lost anything in his telling and we must not take every word as gospel. 'I was once coming through a covert that was flanked by a meadow that sloped to a long rough hedge along which an absent-minded-looking man wandered while a terrier worked it. Presently the terrier turned out a rabbit which bolted for the covert. The terrier made no attempt to chase it. Then I saw in the ditch by the wood side that there peeped, crouched and crept a snaky-looking long dog. It watched for the rabbit's arrival, timed itself to a yard, pounced and killed it with one noiseless wrench, left it in the bottom and moved on parallel with its master.'

The point that a lurcher will kill a rabbit with one movement is repeated in the second verse of the old song, writer unknown, with which I began this chapter.

> We sees the stars twinkle,
> We sees the moon shine,
> We hears the chimes tinkle
> The half after nine
> (Like pigeons the church her
> Sweet chimes throws so good),
> We chirrups the lurcher
> An' goes to Long Wood.
>
> We picks up a rabbit,
> 'Twill never be missed,
> We hears the dog grab it
> An' kill with a twist.

Whilst using a dog is an effective and quiet method, it is, like ferreting, not very productive. In fact, poaching any quantity of rabbits is harder than poaching pheasants, which conveniently settle in a bare tree at dusk and wait for poachers to knock them down. Snaring, at first thought, is an attractive technique for the poacher, for the equipment is simple, light to carry, and leaves almost no trace. So it is if restricted to a few snares in quiet places, but otherwise the risk of discovery is considerable. With a net poachers can come and go in an hour or so but snares have to be set at dusk and lifted at dawn. Even worse, once the snares are spotted all the keeper has to do is hide nearby. The same drawbacks applied to the old gin trap, which never had the same popularity with poachers as the snare, being heavier to carry and much more expensive. All in all rabbit poaching is far from easy, particularly nowadays when rabbits are relatively scarce. Modern rabbit poachers may perhaps think with envy of the last century when vast rabbit populations were concentrated in warrens, but a glimpse at Simpson will show the drawback to high density populations. 'His [the poacher's] attention, when at work, is about equally divided between the keepers and the rabbits. He knows the former cannot be in two places at once, and he works accordingly, but a warren, however large, is much more easily overlooked and guarded, and although the haul be tempting, the risk of the police court is about an even balance. The barbed wire is also a formidable obstacle; and alarm-guns, which are readily put down, provoke the poacher to wrath. He pretends he can find in the dark the slender copper wire attached to the guns, by means of a plummet which he carries before him, and snip it; but he has seldom time to take so much trouble—and besides, a clever keeper can set the gun to go off both ways.'

A last thought on poaching—illustrators of the old school were very fond of depicting the poacher at work in snowy conditions. In practice, nothing could be worse for poaching. It may keep the keeper indoors, but it alters the habits of the rabbits and greatly encumbers the use of wire, net and ferret. Perhaps, worst of all, it shows that the poacher has been, where he came from and where he went.

CHAPTER ELEVEN

Rabbit-Stew

This chapter, as the name suggests, is a mixture of bits and pieces. They have no obvious home, but the book would be incomplete without them.

In the previous chapter I dealt with laws intended to eliminate poaching, and this is a convenient point to list, briefly, those laws intended to reduce rather than eliminate rabbits. Several of these Acts have been touched on previously, but for the sake of convenience I will list them all.

The Ground Game Act of 1880 had more effect on rabbits than any other event outside myxomatosis. Very few tenant farmers enjoyed the sporting rights of the ground they farmed and they were forbidden to kill rabbits as the owners were happy to see a large population, both for sport and profit. A great deal of ill-feeling arose from this situation, for the damage done to the tenants' crops by the rabbits could be immense and the tenants were powerless to stop them. The Act was 'passed in the interest of good husbandry, for the better security of capital and labour invested in the cultivation of the soil, and to enable occupiers to protect their crops from injury by ground game'. The effect of the Act is to give the 'occupier' the right to take ground game, concurrently with whoever may have the sporting rights, and no agreement, irrespective of its wording, can deny this right to an occupier. In addition to his own right the 'occupier' can also give permission to one other person, but this must be in writing. Strictly speaking the harvest field shoots, when you may see half a dozen or more Guns surrounding the corn, are illegal, for the maximum would be two. In practice few shooting tenants, seeking the co-operation of the farmer towards their pheasants and partridges, would even murmur a protest.

One of the major flaws of the Ground Game Act 1880 was its failure to protect an owner or tenant from damage caused by his neighbour's rabbits. An attempt to remedy this was made in 1917, when a Rabbit Order was included in Regulation 2 R of the Defence of the Realm Act, which gave the War Agricultural Executive Committees, and later the Board of Agriculture, unprecedented powers to stop rabbit damage. These were rescinded after the war, but the seeds of the principle of compelling land occupiers to control their rabbit population had been sown and were to flower in subsequent legislation in 1939. Before then many attempts had been made to pass various Rabbit Bills through the House of Commons, at one stage coupling rabbit and rook control together. None of these were successful, mainly through lack of Parliamentary time, but a Select Committee, convened in 1934, produced recommendations which resulted in the Prevention of Damage by Rabbits Act of 1939. Under this County and Local Authorities could require landowners to destroy the rabbits on their land.

With the war over there was time to examine the legal position once more, and the Prevention of Damage by Rabbits Act of 1939 was replaced by Section 98 of the Agricultural Act, 1947. This transferred the power to call for the destruction of rabbits from the County and Local Authorities to the Minister of Agriculture, Fisheries and Food. Here the legal situation rested until the arrival of myxomatosis stimulated new measures in the form of the Pest Act of 1954, which enables the Minister to designate 'rabbit clearance areas'—that is, zones in which every practical step has to be taken to eliminate wild rabbits by the occupier. In fact, the whole of England and Wales has been declared a rabbit clearance area, but the rabbits have refused to co-operate and the population is growing steadily. This Act also makes it an offence to spread myxomatosis.

An interesting question is whether it is necessary to have a game licence before shooting rabbits. Most shooting men believe it is not but, in fact, it is. An Act passed on 13 August 1860, entitled 'An Act to repeal the Duties on Game Certificates and Certificates to deal in Game, and to impose in lieu thereof Duties on Excise Licences and Certificates for the like purposes', laid down an annual fee of £3 for a licence to take or kill game, and 'conies' were specifically listed. In due course the 1880 Ground Game Act removed the need for a Game Licence for any person killing rabbits on enclosed land with the permission of the occupier, and this and other exceptions means that for practical purposes a Licence is rarely necessary. Whatever the legal position there can be very few men who buy a game licence if their shooting is restricted to rabbits and the occasional pigeon.

Because the business of pursuing rabbits goes back many centuries the techniques and equipment have gathered around them many traditions, and the pleasures are enhanced if you make your own equipment. Snares can be made easily, but the most satisfying items are nets. I was taught by an old Derbyshire man and the smell of the twine brings back memories. Once you learn the technique both purse and long-nets are easily made, but I do urge you to get the right materials. The cost of these is so low and the labour involved so high that it is foolish to save a few coppers and produce an inferior job. All will be made clear if you obtain a copy of *Net Making for All* by Charles Holdgate, and published by Mills & Boon, Ltd. (1970).

Having dealt with so many ways of taking rabbits it is appropriate to consider eating them. Once they have been paunched, and harled, hocked or legged, as you please, they may be hung, but not for long; indeed, if the weather is warm a day or so is long enough.

So far as cooking is concerned there is no shortage of suggestions. The Lonsdale Library's *Shooting* starts its advice on fried rabbit with a ring of days now past. 'If your cook is a good hand at a fry . . .' Mine, I am pleased to report, is. (She is also a good hand at a typewriter, as a result of which this hand-written manuscript will eventually reach the publishers in readable form.) However, whether yours works for money or love, she must dry and joint the rabbit, fry it in butter until nearly done, then drain and cool the sections. They must then be thickly covered in egg and breadcrumbs and fried, golden brown, in very hot olive oil.

Success with any rabbit dish depends upon selecting the right rabbit, for the young are obviously tender while the old are not only tougher but also dry. Boiled rabbit can be ghastly, particularly when cooked by young men on a survival course or the equivalent. (I think it was when I was living rough for a few days in the High Peak of Derbyshire and cooking the rabbits I snared that the first flickering thoughts of marriage crossed my bachelor mind.)

Somewhat cynically, I decided to compare the three books in my collection most informative on rabbit cookery, expecting to find that little progress had been made in the last century. In fact, excepting the standard stewing, roasting and boiling, hardly a dish was repeated. I will not trouble you with lengthy instructions, for if your wife is so-minded in these matters she will have cookery books by the shelf, and if she is not she will not read this. However, a few general details are interesting, if only to show what can be done with such a mundane thing as a rabbit. Lonsdale's *Shooting* suggests several forms of stews, including using Burgundy, and even milk and mushrooms. Harting includes a full twenty-seven pages on the subject, in a chapter by Alexander Innes Shand. A careful study suggests Harting knew what he was about when he selected Mr. Shand for the job, for it is a masterly piece full of authoritative pronouncements on, for example, ways of making the best mushroom sauce for rabbits, quoting Meg Dodds, and then commenting, 'It is a good sauce but, far from needing to strengthen the mushroom flavour, in our opinion it is essentially too strong. It somewhat oppresses the sweet simplicity of the rabbit, whereas, etc.,' and much more in the vein of a man who knows his onions in every sense.

But if you really want your wife to become an expert at rabbit cookery, or for that matter, any other form of game, there are two excellent books to buy her. One is *The Game Cookery Book* (1975), compiled for The Game Conservancy by Julia Drysdale. This is a superb book in every way and the chapter on the rabbit has enough variations for you to feed regularly on rabbits for a year without becoming bored. In one sentence Mrs Drysdale gives the secret of rabbit cookery, 'As they have little natural fat, rabbits must be well barded or larded and cooked with plenty of butter or oil.' A brief list of a few variations will give you some idea of the range: sweet and sour rabbit; optional rabbit; Swedish curried rabbit; rabbit my way (Mrs Bo Thelander); fricassee of rabbit; rabbit in red wine; rabbit with onions; rabbit with apples; rabbit with mustard; rabbit with tarragon; rabbit with black grapes and tomatoes; rabbit villettes.

The second book, never absent from my wife's kitchen, is Barbara Hargreaves's *The Sporting Wife* (1971), and this also offers a large range of alternative rabbit dishes. There are Harvest rabbits; rabbits rolled in castor sugar; rabbits with prunes; curried rabbits; rabbits in mustard; and even savory rabbit giblets.

Harting, as usual, deserves the last word. 'Finally the head is not to be neglected. It contains a variety of delicate pickings, and gives light, desultory occupation to a wayward appetite.'

Apart from attempting briefly to forecast the future of the rabbit (there is no need to ponder on the ferret, for its fortunes are inexorably tied to the rabbit), I have finished my work. When I first contemplated this book I envisaged it heavily sprinkled with personal experiences; in the event they have been crowded out by the weight of more factual material, and it is only now that I can dwell, briefly, on the pleasure and interest I have had from rabbits and ferrets. I am in good company, for it is noticeable how every shooting writer begins his chapter on rabbiting in a relaxed style. Consider Payne-Gallwey, one of the finest shots of his era, and a man whose bag of pheasants ran into the tens of thousands: 'Of the various beasts or fowls of chase or warren which have been treated of in this work, there is none which affords more universal sport and amusement than the common rabbit.'

Although I have shot rabbits in most parts of this country, my principal recollections are of younger days in Norfolk, and later Derbyshire. Only those who knew Norfolk in pre-myxie times will really appreciate the vast numbers of rabbits to be viewed, driving quietly around the countryside on a summer evening. Heaven for me was following my uncle's footsteps as he hunted out the hedgerows and the wood fringes with a ·410 and a spaniel, but the peak of the year was the harvest fields. Here, armed with just a stick, I would run down the rabbits as they bolted from the corn for the cover of the hedge. Improbable as this may sound it was perfectly feasible, for the stubble slowed rabbits to the point where a fit youngster could overtake them. The Norfolk of those days was an enclosed world of small, well-hedged fields and Derbyshire was an extreme contrast. So were the weather conditions. Gone was the heat of August, with straw hats and the thinnest of shirts, to be replaced by keen winds drifting curtains of snow over the High Peak, while I crouched under a dry stone wall and cursed the ferret. Digging was often impossible for the rabbits frequently burrowed among stone-covered hillsides, or even lived among a litter of fallen stone.

It was my love of the Derbyshire hills that led me to the Hebrides and some fine rabbit shooting. The ferreting in these distant and romantic islands can be excellent, for the ground is open and there are none of the low-ground problems of thick cover to snag nets and conceal bolting rabbits. In fact, I have mainly left the ferreting to my sons, for my own love has been the hill-tops and the grouse, but the evenings have seen great sport among the bracken. Where the cultivated ground of the crofters gives way to the great oceans of heather there is usually a wide belt of bracken, frequently dotting the hillside in various sized clumps. These shelter rabbit populations of differing sizes, depending on the last outbreak of myxie but, at their best, I have seen nothing like it since the old Norfolk days. The technique is to work the bracken from below so the rabbits bolt uphill, giving very tricky snap-shooting as they cross the open spaces. As the hillsides are often steep the angle of the gun often suggests pheasants rather than rabbit shooting, and a cleanly killed rabbit will often roll back down the hill to your feet.

My earliest memories of ferrets concern my mother. In pre-war Norfolk, rats were a major problem and each farm in our area had its annual rat day, when all the neighbours would concentrate for a combined onslaught, which was as much a social occasion as an exercise in vermin control. Every visitor brought at least one ferret and when this small army was turned loose into the farm buildings there was great excitement and confusion. From time to time ferrets would emerge sorely wounded, and my mother's task was to tend them. I see her now sponging wounds with warm water and an antiseptic, the while talking gently to the ferrets.

Naturally I wanted my own ferret, but my father ruled otherwise. By the time we moved to Derbyshire, and I was in serious pursuit of the local rabbits, my ambition was intense but for months success or failure depended on an old, fat, congenial ferret belonging to a companion. The fire of this beast's enthusiasm may be judged by the fact that when snow lay on the hills it would often lie up in an empty burrow rather than face the cold. Eventually an exceptionally frustrating day coincided with meeting an elderly quarry worker in a small village. He had a ferret to sell which was, he swore, as strong as a lion and fierce with it. By the light of the single street lamp the ferret, a large powerful polecat, was displayed. I peered at the long white teeth, strong claws and large bright eyes and yielded. For five shillings I received the ferret plus a small sack and a handful of straw. I put the two items into the one, slung the sack over my shoulder and, as I cycled the long miles home over the hills, pondered on how to persuade my father to accept the new addition to the home. I was still pondering when I reached the rear entrance. It was obvious that something more subtle was needed than bursting in with the beast so I laid the sack on the ground in a corner of the unlit coal cellar.

In the event negotiations went surprisingly well. Preoccupied with other matters he put up only a token resistance, and within minutes I rushed out to the coal cellar and felt in the dark corner for my prize. Meanwhile the ferret had been far from dormant. The bumpy ride had no doubt subdued it, but left alone it had rapidly bitten a hole in the sack and thrust its head through, at which point it had stuck. Now, bewildered and very cross, it encountered a thing moving around the floor. In one sharp snap its fangs met through the fleshy part of my right forefinger, and some minutes passed before it could be persuaded to let go. Rarely has a father been able to say 'I told you so' with a stronger ring of self-righteousness.

In fact, it was a good ferret and when it eventually passed on to the well-stocked rabbit burrow where, doubtless, all good ferrets go, I wept and was inconsolable for days. Others followed it, including the pair which tunnelled under both their run and the boundary wall to emerge in our neighbour's hen run. Fortunately they were discovered when the death toll was only three but, in my circumstances, even this came expensive.

Perhaps the strangest encounter with a ferret came on the Isle of Mull. My boys and I were in an isolated part of that rather isolated island when we came across a decent looking burrow and popped in a ferret. After a minute or so's silence there came a great commotion, and our ferret shot out in alarm to be followed by another ferret, obviously in a state of high indignation. It paused at the entrance to its violated home for a few seconds, chattering violently, then, having seen off the intruder, went below again. In East Anglia this would have been worthy of comment, but no more; in the Hebrides where ferrets are very rare it was remarkable.

What then of the future? Myxomatosis will not exterminate the rabbit; nor is it likely that a combination of the disease and the efforts of man will, for if they failed when myxie had reduced the rabbit population to its lowest level for many years, they cannot succeed now. The simple proof of this is that Australia still has a serious rabbit problem. Judging from the course of the disease in Brazil it is quite possible that myxomatosis will eventually become a permanent, non-lethal disease in British rabbits. However, if this occurs it will take a long time and the likelihood is that myxomatosis will exercise the major control over rabbit numbers for at least the remainder of this century.

Rabbits and ferrets have played their modest, but by no means inconsiderable, part in the sporting scene for many generations past and, writing as a sportsman, it is a happy thought that many generations hence they will still be held in the same regard by our descendants.

Select Bibliography

A. B. C. of Shooting, The, ed. by Colin Willock, André Deutsch, London, 1975

Adams, Richard, *Watership Down*, Rex Collings, London, 1972

Barkley, H. C., *Studies in the Art of Rat-Catching*, John Murray, London, 1896

Barret-Hamilton, *see* Hamilton

Beirne, Bryan Patrick, *The Origin and History of the British Fauna*, Methuen, London, 1952

Bewick, Thomas, *A Natural History of British Quadrupeds*, W. Davidson, Alnwick, [1814]

Blome, Richard, *The Gentlemans Recreation*, S. Roycroft, London, 1686

Book of St. Albans or *The Book of Hawking, Hunting and Blasing of Arms*, [St. Albans, 1486]; another edition, Westminster, W. de Worde, 1496

Boutcher, William, *A Treatise on Forest Trees*, pub. by author, Edinburgh, 1775

Cansdale, George Soper, *Animals and Man*, Hutchinson, London, 1952

Carnegie, William, *Practical Trapping*, 'The Bazaar', London, [1880], reprinted by Tideline Books, 1973

Chalmers, Patrick, *At the Sign of the Dog and Gun*, Philip Allan, London, 1930

The Frequent Gun, Philip Allan, London, 1928

The Shooting-Man's England, Seeley Service, London, 1936

Colquhoun, John, *The Moor and the Loch*, 4th edition, William Blackwood, London, 1878

Drysdale, Julia, *The Game Cookery Book*, Collins, London, 1975

Everitt, Nicholas, *Ferrets: Their Management in Health and Disease*, R. A. Everett & Son, London, 1906

Haggard, Lilias Rider, ed., *I Walked by Night*, Nicholson & Watson, London, 1935

Hamilton, G. E. H. Barrett-, and Martin A. C. Hinton, *A History of British Mammals*, Gurney & Jackson, London, 1910-21

Hargreaves, Barbara, *The Sporting Wife*, Witherby, London, 1971

Harting, James Edmund, *Hints on Shore Shooting*, London, 1871

The Rabbit ... with a chapter on cookery by A. I. Shand, (Fur, Feather and Fin Series), Longmans, London, 1898

Hawker, Peter, *The Diary of Col. P. Hawker, 1802–1853*, with an introduction by Sir R. Payne-Gallwey, Bart., Longmans, London, 1893

Instructions to Young Sportsmen, 3rd edition, Longmans, London, 1824

Head, Sir George, *A Home Tour Through the Manufacturing Districts of England in the Summer of 1835*, London, 1836

Holdgate, Charles, *Net Making for All*, Mills & Boon, London, 1970

Jefferies, Richard, *The Gamekeeper at Home: Sketches of Natural History and Rural Life*, Smith Elder, London, 1880

Jones, Owen and Marcus Woodward, *A Gamekeeper's Note-Book*, Edward Arnold, London, 1910

Jones, Owen, *The Sport of Shooting*, 2nd edition, Edward Arnold, London, 1928

Lawrence, Richard, *The Complete Farrier and British Sportsman*, Thomas Kelly, London, 1831

Lockley, Ronald Mathias, *The Private Life of the Rabbit*, André Deutsch, London, 1964; Corgi paperback, 1973

Markham, Gervase, *Hungers Prevention: Or, The Whole Arte of Fowling by Water and Land*, A. Math[ewes], London, 1621

Maison Rustique: Or The Countrey Farme ... Now ... augmented by G. Markham, 1616; original edition, 1600, by C. Estienne

Marshall, William, *The Rural Economy of Yorkshire: Comprizing the Management of Landed Estates, and the Present Practice of Husbandry in the Agricultural Districts of that County*, London, 1788

'Martingale' [White], *Sporting Scenes and Country Characters*, Longmans, London, 1840

Mascall, Leonard, *A Booke of Fishing with Hooke and Line; Another of Sundrie Engines and Trappes to take Polcats, Buzards, Rattes*, [London], 1590

Matthews, L. Harrison, *British Mammals*, (New Naturalist Series), Collins, London, 1952

Mead-Briggs, A. R., 'The reproductive biology of the rabbit flea *Spilopsyllus cuniculi* (Dale) and the dependence of this species upon the breeding of its host, *Journal of Experimental Biology* 41 (1964), 371–402.

Millais, J. G., *British Deer and Their Horns*, London, Southeran, 1897

Niall, Ian, *The New Poachers' Handbook*, Heinemann, London, 1960

Niblett, Arthur and the Editor of *The Exchange and Mart*, *Ferrets and Ferreting*, 7th edition, Bazaar, Exchange and Mart, London, [1934]; fifteen editions from 1875 to 1953 with various contributors

Oke, George C., *A Handy Book of the Game and Fishery Laws: Containing all the Acts in Force as to Game, Rabbits, etc.*, Butterworths, London, 1861

Parker, Eric, *Elements of Shooting*, Field Press, London, 1924

Shooting by Moor, Field and Shore, (Lonsdale Library), London, Seeley Service, 1951

Payne-Gallwey, Sir Ralph, Bart., *Letters to Young Shooters*, 4th edition, Longmans, London, 1895

Payne-Gallwey, Sir Ralph, Bart. and Thomas De Grey, 6th Baron Walsingham, *Shooting: Field and Covert*, 3rd edition, Longmans, London, 1889

Price, Lloyd, *Rabbits for Profit and Rabbits for Powder*, H. Cox, London, 1884

Romanes, G. J., *The Natural History of Instinct*, Sunday Lecture Society, 1886

Animal Intelligence, 3rd edition, Kegan Paul & Co., London, 1883

Row, Charles, *A Practical Guide to the Game Laws*, Longmans, London, 1907

Ryves, Benjamin Harvey, *Bird Life in Cornwall*, Collins, London, 1948

St. John, Charles, *Short Sketches of Wild Sports and Natural History of the Highlands*, John Murray, London, 1879

Samuel, E. and J. Ivester Lloyd, *Rabbiting and Ferreting*, 5th edition, British Field Sports Society, 1972

Sedgwick, Noel M., *Wildfowling and Rough Shooting*, Herbert Jenkins, London, 1950

The Young Shot, A. & C. Black, London, 1940

Sedgwick, Noel M., Peter Whitaker and Jeffrey Harrison, *The New Wildfowler in the 1970s*, Barrie & Jenkins, London, 1961

Sheail, John, *Rabbits and Their History*, David & Charles, London, 1971

Simpson, J., *The Wild Rabbit in a New Aspect or Rabbit-Warrens that Pay*, 2nd edition, William Blackwood, Edinburgh, 1895

Southern, H. N., *The Handbook of British Mammals*, Mammal Society of the British Isles, 1964

H. N. Southern began a three-year investigation into rabbit ecology and behaviour in 1938 by studying a warren at Sheepstead, Berkshire when he was with the Bureau of Animal Population, Oxford University. This, and subsequent work, produced important results which were published in the following papers:

'Coprophagy in the wild rabbit', *Nature* 145 (1940a), 262

'The ecology and population dynamics of the wild rabbit, *Oryctolagus cuniculus*', *Annals of Applied Biology* 27 (1940b), 509–26

'Periodicity of reflection in the wild rabbit', *Nature* 149 (1942), 553

'Sexual and aggressive behaviour in the wild rabbit', *Behaviour* 1 (1948), 173–94

with Watson, J. S., 'The summer food of the red fox (*Vulpes vulpes*) in Great Britain: a preliminary report', *Journal of Animal Ecology* 10 (1941), 1–11

Speakman, F. J., *A Poacher's Tale*, ed. by A. T. Curtis, G. Bell, London, 1960

Teasdale-Buckell, G. T., *The Complete Shot*, Methuen, London, 1907

Tennyson, C. Julian, *Rough Shooting*, A. & C. Black, London, 1938

Thomas, William, *Rabbit Shooting to Ferrets*, Hutchinsons, London, 1946

Thompson, Harry V. and Alastair N. Worden, *The Rabbit*, (New Naturalist Series), Collins, London, 1956

Turner, T. W., *Memoirs of a Gamekeeper*, Geoffrey Bles, London, 1954

Van den Brink, F. H., *A Field Guide to the Mammals of Britain and Europe*, trans. Hans Kruuk, ed. H. N. Southern, Collins, London, 1967

Whitaker, Peter H., *Approach to Shooting*, Burlington Publishing Co., London, 1942

Willett, Roderick and Gurney A. Grattan, *Rough Shooting*, new edition, Faber & Faber, London, 1975

Index